# QUANTUM
# COMPUTING
## EXPLAINED FOR BEGINNERS

*The Science, Technology, and Impact*

## PANTHEON SPACE ACADEMY

# QUANTUM
## COMPUTING
### EXPLAINED FOR BEGINNERS

# PANDORA'S BOX OF QUANTUM QUESTIONS

Are Quantum computers real? Introduction to classical and quantum computing. Quantum computation and quantum information. Quantum computing book. Quantum computing pdf. Quantum computing an applied approach. Quantum computing and AI. Quantum computing and artificial intelligence. Quantum computing architecture. Quantum computing fundamentals.

Quantum computing basics. Quantum computing applications. Quantum computing Cambridge. Quantum computing introduction. Introduction to Quantum Computing. Quantum computing Chuang. Quantum computing mike. Quantum computing book kaku. Quantum computing brian clegg. Quantum computing mug. Quantum computing nakahara.

How quantum computing works. What is quantum computing? Who invented quantum computing? Are quantum computers faster? When will quantum computers be available? What is quantum computing used for? What can quantum computers do? Where quantum computing is used. Quantum computing with AI.

Quantum Computing for dummies. Quantum computing for everyone. Quantum computing jobs near me. Quantum computing without quantum computers. Quantum computing for computer scientists. Quantum computing for the very curious. Quantum computing as a service. Quantum computing companies. Quantum Computing in action.

Quantum computing help the world. Quantum computing break encryption. Quantum computing benefits and risk. Quantum computing cryptography. Quantum computing function. Quantum computing blockchain. Quantum computing fundamentals. Quantum computing discovery. Quantum computing skill development.

Quantum computing simple terms. Quantum computing finance. Quantum computing investing. IBM quantum computer. Quantum computing healthcare. Quantum computing stocks. Quantum computing hacking. Quantum computing government. Quantum computing training.

The map of Quantum computing. Mapping Quantum computing. Quantum computer race. Quantum Supremacy. Quantum computing terms. Quantum computing updates. Quantum computer absolute zero. Quantum computing startups. Quantum computing speed. Quantum computing mechanics. Quantum computing course.

Quantum computing open source. Quantum computing degree. Quantum computing online. Quantum computing lectures. Quantum computing labs. Quantum computing limitations. Quantum computing leaders. Quantum computing learning. Quantum computing meaning. Quantum computing masters. Quantum computing medicine.

Quantum computing news. Quantum computing network. Quantum computing optimization. Quantum computing overview. Quantum computing oracle. Quantum computing programming. Quantum computing professors. Quantum computing paper. Quantum computing public. Quantum computing questions and answers. Quantum computing q & a. Quantum computing report.

Quantum computing regulations. Quantum computing roadmap. Quantum computing research. Quantum computing risks. Quantum computing revolution. Quantum computing salary. Quantum computing scientist. Quantum computing timeline. Quantum computing workshop. Quantum computing python. How quantum computers work. Who invented quantum computers?

# TABLE OF CONTENTS

# INTRODUCTION

In human history, there have been moments—just mere blips in the timeline of our existence—where our understanding of the universe has been radically changed. Think of the moment Copernicus realized that the Earth revolves around the sun or when Einstein unveiled the theory of relativity. We're at the threshold of yet another transformative shift—the world of quantum computing.

The buzzwords "quantum" and "computing" have likely found your ears, either in passing conversations or in the latest tech articles. But what does it all mean? The answer is both profound and simple: quantum computing, with its flashy principles of superposition and entanglement, promises to redefine our future. From altering how we approach complex problems to reshaping industries, the quantum wave will leave no stone unturned.

Why trust my voice over the hundreds of existing quantum forums? Because I've navigated the maze of quantum jargon and emerged not just unscathed but inspired. I've translated this highly technical subject into actionable insights for tech companies, classrooms, and entrepreneurs. My journey, filled with breathtaking turns and stops at enlightening landmarks, has been distilled into this book. As your guide, I will walk you through the world of quantum computing, making sure that complex concepts are accessible by breaking them down into simple language.

But the larger question remains: Why should you care? The reality is that understanding quantum computing is about more than just keeping up with new trends. It's about preparing for a future that's unfolding before us, a future where those not in the know might find themselves playing catch-up. Whether you're a student, a teacher, a tech-lover, or just very curious about cool new stuff, this book is for you. You're not just going to read about quantum computing; you're going to visit The Quantum Continent to explore the digital landscape and find treasure!

Just ten years ago, this was the stuff of science fiction. Today, it's a reality that has enormous potential to shape industries, solve unlikely problems, and even transform global issues like hunger or diseases. Quantum computing will change the world in ways we have yet to imagine. At the same time, quantum systems are still in their early stages. Many challenges must be overcome before we can realize its full potential. Building a quantum computing empire will require a group effort from governments, academia, and industry.

This book is your compass to gain a comprehensive introduction to the field of quantum computing, from its foundational principles to its practical applications. We'll start with the basic concepts of quantum mechanics and how they relate to quantum computers vs. classical computers. From there, we'll tour the architecture of quantum computing: hardware and software components, including qubits, quantum gates, and quantum algorithms.

You'll also explore the power of quantum computing in cryptography, machine learning, and optimization. I discuss how quantum computers can solve problems that classical computers can't and explore the potential impact of quantum computing on careers and AI.

In addition to the technical aspects of quantum computing, the last chapter is a thought exercise on the ethical and societal implications of this emerging technology. You will think about issues like data privacy, cybersecurity, and the potential impact of quantum computing on employment, government, and your neighbors.

By the end of this book, you'll have a solid grasp of quantum computing fundamentals, applications, and as a service. You won't just be observing from the sidelines—you'll actively participate in the excitement with our included Quantum Toolkit. It's packed with hands-on resources waiting for you to take control.

So, with heartfelt enthusiasm, I invite you to join me on this quest. This isn't just another tech read; it's a shared adventure into the quantum environment that promises knowledge and a vision of what's to come. Ready? Let's unite and unlock the future together.

# CHAPTER 1

## THE PHYSICS OF QUANTUM COMPUTERS

While classical computing has revolutionized our world, making the unimaginable tangible, it remains confined by its foundational, classical laws. Yet, beneath this camouflage lies a more mystifying empire governed by the characteristics of quantum mechanics.

Embark on an expedition into (my analogy) the Quantum Continent—a land where the usual rules give way to the captivating quirks of the quantum world. Together, we'll navigate the vast plains of superposition, climb the towering cliffs of quantum tunneling, and sail the unpredictable rivers of quantum entanglement.

By the time we're through, you'll have a comprehensive understanding of quantum mechanics and a profound appreciation for the foundation upon which the future of computing stands.

Prepare yourself, intrepid explorer. The Quantum Continent awaits, and we're about to set foot on its mesmerizing terrains, uncovering secrets that have puzzled and amazed the brightest minds for decades. Let the expedition begin!

# Explaining The Fundamental Principles Of Quantum Mechanics

*Introduction to Quantum Mechanics and Quantum Computing*

Quantum mechanics is a branch of physics that delves deep into the behavior of particles at the atomic and subatomic scales. This revolutionary field of study has shifted our perspective, transforming our understanding of the fundamental nature of reality. While classical physics offers explanations for the macroscopic world we see and interact with daily, quantum mechanics takes us on a journey to the microscopic dimensions where particles can exist in multiple states simultaneously, communicate over vast distances instantaneously, and generally defy common sense.

Enter quantum computing, a burgeoning field that harnesses the mind-bending properties of quantum mechanics to process information in ways previously thought impossible. Traditional, or classical computers, use bits as the smallest unit of data—either a 0 or a 1. Quantum computers, on the other hand, make use of quantum bits, or qubits. Thanks to principles like superposition and entanglement, these qubits allow quantum computers to perform tasks and solve problems classical computers struggle with or cannot handle.

*Key Principles of Quantum Mechanics in Computing*

1. **Superposition**: One of the cornerstones of quantum mechanics is the idea of superposition. To envision superposition, consider the famous thought experiment known as Schrödinger's Cat. In this

mental exercise, a cat inside a sealed box is simultaneously alive and dead until we observe it, at which point it collapses into one of the states. Similarly, a qubit can simultaneously be in a superposition of 0 and 1 states, collapsing into a definite state only upon measurement.

2.    **Qubits**: As the fundamental unit of quantum information, qubits can exist in a superposition of states. This capability allows quantum computers to process a massive amount of data simultaneously, potentially offering exponential speed-ups for specific problems compared to classical counterparts.

3.    **Entanglement**: Another counterintuitive but integral concept in quantum mechanics is entanglement. When particles become entangled, one particle's state instantly influences another's state, regardless of the distance separating them. This interconnected behavior is essential for quantum computers, enabling more complex and intertwined computational processes.

*Harnessing Quantum Mechanics in Computing:*

The promise of quantum computing is profound. For instance, algorithms like Shor's can factorize large numbers more efficiently than the best-known classical algorithms—a capability with profound implications for cryptography. However, building a functional quantum computer is no small feat. Various technological approaches are being explored, from gate-based ion trap processors manipulated by lasers to superconducting processors at cryogenic temperatures, each with unique advantages and challenges.

Quantum will initially seem perplexing; it represents a frontier of endless possibilities. As our understanding of quantum mechanics deepens, and our capabilities in quantum computing expand, we stand on the cusp of a new computational era, potentially reshaping our technological and scientific landscape.

## Wave-Particle Duality

In the classical world we know, an object is defined by its intrinsic properties. A football is a particle. It's tangible, solid, and you can kick it. The ripples in a pond? They behave as waves, spreading outward in concentric circles when a stone is tossed. But enter the domain of the subatomic, and the lines blur. Quantum mechanics presents a thrilling challenge to these notions.

Imagine, if you will, that same football, not just being kicked around the field, but also creating ripples like those in a pond. It's a perplexing thought, isn't it? This is the heart of wave-particle duality. In the quantum world, entities like electrons don't confine themselves to being "just a particle" or "just a wave." They might exhibit both characteristics depending on how we measure or observe them.

### Implications in Quantum Computing

When considering quantum computing, the essence of wave-particle duality becomes incredibly potent. One must grasp this concept to leverage qubits' true power. Qubits aren't confined to the strict binary states like classical bits; thanks to the principles of duality, they can be both 0 and 1 until measured.

## Probabilistic Nature of Quantum Mechanics

Imagine standing at a crossroads on your expedition through the Quantum Continent, a thick fog surrounding you. There are many paths leading in different directions, but the fog hides where each one goes. You know that once you start walking, one of the paths will become your reality, but until that moment, all paths remain possibilities.

This analogy encapsulates the quantum world's inherent uncertainty. Unlike flipping a light switch, where the outcome is a definite "on" or "off", quantum mechanics leans into probability. One of the most famous thought experiments to explain this is Schrödinger's Cat. A cat inside a sealed box is simultaneously alive and dead, a superposition of states, until we open the box and observe, collapsing the state to a single reality.

*Implications in Quantum Computing*

This understanding is vital for quantum computers, which thrive on this uncertainty. Algorithms in quantum computers operate on the principle that qubits can be in superpositions of states, allowing for vast computations in parallel. When we finally "measure" or read out the qubit, it collapses to a definitive state.

## Quantization of Energy Levels

As you journey further into the Quantum Continent, imagine stumbling upon a mystical jukebox. But there's a catch. The volume knob on this jukebox doesn't allow for minute adjustments. You can't set it to level 2.5 or 3.8. Only whole numbers, discrete levels of volume: 1, 2, 3, and so on.

This is much akin to quantized energy levels in quantum mechanics. Atoms and their electrons don't have a continuous energy spectrum. Instead, they can only exist in certain, fixed energy states. Much like the jukebox, there's no "in-between."

*Significance in Quantum Computing*

The importance of quantization becomes clear when we think about qubits and their manipulations. By understanding and harnessing these discrete energy levels, quantum computers can effectively manipulate qubits, transitioning them between their quantized states to perform computations.

As we navigate the Quantum Continent, observing its marvels, these principles serve as our guiding compass. They shed light on the mysterious behaviors of the quantum realm and, more crucially, lay the foundation for understanding quantum computers' immense power and potential.

## Wave-Particle Duality

*Beyond Traditional Boundaries*

Imagine you're wandering the landscapes of our Quantum Continent and stumble upon an enigmatic creature: a chameleon. This isn't any ordinary chameleon, though. One moment it's solid, moving on the ground like any typical reptile. But in an instant, it transforms, flowing like water, gracefully navigating the terrain's intricacies. This chameleon's ability to change its nature represents the wave-particle duality found in quantum mechanics.

However, pausing and reflecting is essential as you marvel at this creature. Quantum mechanics gives us the tools to understand these unique behaviors, harnessing them for quantum computing. Yet, the answers are more elusive when it comes to more profound "why" questions about the nature of such quantum phenomena. These mysteries still spark philosophical and scientific discussions, reminding us that quantum physics has many secrets yet to unveil.

*Understanding the Dual Nature*

The quantum realm is rife with counterintuitive phenomena, and wave-particle duality is a prime example. It stems from experiments where particles, like electrons, displayed wave-like behavior under certain conditions. In the iconic double-slit experiment, for instance, electrons shot toward a barrier with two slits produce an interference pattern on the other side, as waves would. However, when observed more closely, these electrons appear as distinct particles, landing as individual points.

*Relevance to Quantum Computing*

Wave-particle duality is pivotal to quantum computing for several reasons:

1. **State Representation:** The duality allows qubits to be in a superposition, where they simultaneously exist in multiple states. Unlike classical bits, which are firmly a 0 or a 1, qubits harness their

wave-like nature to represent a multitude of possibilities, enabling vast parallelism in computation.

2.   **Interference as a Resource:** Just as the double-slit experiment showcases interference in waves, quantum algorithms utilize interference to amplify correct solutions and diminish wrong ones. Quantum computers leverage this duality-driven interference to arrive at solutions faster than their classical counterparts.

3.   **Quantum Gates and Operations:** The duality principle underpins the very operations performed in a quantum computer. Quantum gates manipulate qubits by exploiting their wave-like properties, causing constructive or destructive interference, akin to merging or diverging waves in an ocean.

Embracing wave-particle duality is akin to the chameleon's ability to adapt and thrive in varied terrains on our Quantum Continent. This duality provides the flexibility and power to outmaneuver traditional computing boundaries in the quantum computing universe. It's not just a quirky behavior but a foundational tenet that propels the essence of quantum computational prowess.

## The Born Rule

*Navigating the Probabilistic Waters of the Quantum Continent*

Deep within the Quantum Continent lies an enigmatic ocean. At first glance, this ocean seems ordinary. However, its waters, representing quantum probabilities, are guided by an unseen but profound force: the Born Rule. Imagine standing at the shores of this vast expanse, peering into its depths and trying to predict the pattern of the waves or the location of a fish. The Born Rule provides the compass and the map to make sense of this unpredictable realm.

*Deciphering the Born Rule*

Named after physicist Max Born, links the mathematical descriptions of quantum systems to the probabilities of various observable outcomes. It states that the probability of a particular measurement outcome corresponds to the square of the magnitude (or absolute value) of the quantum system's wave function in that specific configuration.

In simpler terms, imagine our Quantum Ocean having waves of varying heights. The probability of finding a fish at a specific spot in this ocean isn't determined merely by the height of the wave at that location but by the square of its size. The higher the wave (or amplitude), the greater the likelihood, but the relationship isn't linear—it's a power of two.

*Significance to Quantum Computing*

Understanding the Born Rule is paramount for several reasons:

1.   **Probabilistic Outcomes:** Unlike classical computers, which output definitive results, quantum computers operate in the realm of probabilities. After processing information using qubits, when we measure the outcome, the Born Rule determines the likelihood of each possible result. Knowing this rule is foundational to making sense of these outcomes.

2. **Guiding Quantum Algorithms:** Many quantum algorithms, like Grover's and Shor's, inherently exploit this probabilistic nature. The algorithms manipulate qubits to amplify the probabilities of correct solutions, making them more likely to be observed. This amplification, in essence, is guided by the principles of the Born Rule.

3. **Measurement and Collapse:** In quantum mechanics, measurement leads to the collapse of the wave function, meaning the quantum system settles into a definitive state post-measurement. In this context, the Born Rule governs which state the system will most likely collapse into.

As we navigate the Quantum Continent, the Born Rule is the guiding force allowing us to predict and harness the probabilistic nature of the quantum realm. Quantum computing, at its heart, thrives on uncertainty. But with tools like the Born Rule, this uncertainty is not a hindrance but a superpower. It's a dance of probabilities, where the choreography, complex as it might be, unveils the potential to solve problems that were once deemed insurmountable by classical standards.

*Probabilistic Nature of Quantum Systems and Their Implication in Quantum Computing*

In the realm of classical physics, events unfold predictably. If we roll a ball down a hill, we can estimate where and when it'll come to a stop. The rules governing such macroscopic events are well-understood and deterministic. However, when we zoom into the quantum level, this predictability vanishes, replaced by a cloud of probabilities.

## Wave Functions and Probabilities

At the heart of quantum mechanics is the wave function. Think of it as a mathematical representation that provides a probability distribution of a quantum system's possible states. Instead of saying an electron is "here," we say it's "most likely here." The wave function doesn't describe the exact position of an electron, for example, but instead gives us a probability of finding it in various locations around an atom.

## The Real-World Electron Dilemma

To get a grip on this, consider electrons in an atom. Unlike planets orbiting the sun in distinct paths, electrons exist in "clouds" called orbitals around the nucleus. If you've ever seen an atomic diagram with fuzzy clouds encircling the center, those represent areas where we're most likely to find an electron. But remember, "most likely" doesn't mean "definitely." It's all about chances.

## Quantum Computing's Reliance on Probabilities

So, how does this probabilistic nature tie into quantum computing? Quantum computers operate using qubits, which can be in a superposition of states, unlike classical bits that are always either a 0 or a 1. Essentially, a qubit represents both 0 and 1 simultaneously until it's measured. Upon measurement, the qubit collapses to a 0 or a 1 based on its probability distribution.

This probabilistic behavior gives quantum computers their edge. Being able to process multiple possibilities simultaneously means quantum algorithms can explore many solutions at once. But it also introduces challenges. For instance, the results from quantum computations can be probabilistic, meaning we might have to run them multiple times to get a reliable outcome.

Furthermore, harnessing this probabilistic nature in quantum algorithms can offer computational advantages. When faced with tasks like simulating quantum systems or navigating vast computational landscapes to find optimized solutions, quantum computers leverage their probabilistic behavior to process and evaluate numerous possibilities concurrently.

Grasping the probabilistic essence of quantum systems is paramount to understanding how quantum computers function. This isn't randomness for the sake of chaos; it's a foundational principle of the quantum world. And as we build more advanced quantum computers, this very principle promises to revolutionize computation as we know it.

*Quantization of Energy Levels - The Ladder of Quantum States*

Imagine you're climbing a ladder. Each rung represents a specific height, a distinct step above the ground. You can't stand halfway between two rungs; you're either on one rung or another. In much the same way, in the quantum world, energy isn't continuous but is divided into distinct levels, much like the rungs on a ladder. This is the principle behind the quantization of energy levels.

*Atoms and Their Discrete Dance*

Atoms, the building blocks of matter, contain a nucleus surrounded by electrons. These electrons don't whirl around the core any which way they want; instead, they exist in specific "shells" or "orbitals," each associated with a precise energy level. Think back to the electron clouds we talked about: these aren't random misty patches but are tied to specific energy rungs.

But why does this matter for quantum computers?

*Quantum Bits and Energy Levels*

Quantum computers use qubits, which, in some architectures, are derived from properties of electrons, such as their spin. The distinct energy levels play a pivotal role here. When we manipulate a qubit, we're essentially navigating it through these quantized energy levels. The qubit's information is encoded based on these levels, and the precision with which we can control and measure these states is central to the functioning of a quantum computer.

For example, in quantum computers that use trapped ions as qubits, individual ions are manipulated using lasers. By carefully tuning these lasers, we can make an electron in an ion jump between different energy levels, effectively flipping a qubit between its 0 and 1 state. Here, the quantized nature of energy levels is a blessing, providing a clear, distinct boundary between the two states of the qubit.

## The Power of Discreteness in Quantum Computing

You might ask: why is the quantization of energy so exciting for quantum computing? It ensures precision. In classical computing, we're used to bits being either in a 0 or a 1 state. In quantum computing, qubits can be in a superposition of 0 and 1, but when we measure them, they collapse to one of the states. These definitive, quantized energy levels provide a clear distinction between these states, enabling us to accurately read the results of quantum computations.

Furthermore, how quantum algorithms are designed often leverages the quantized nature of quantum systems. For example, quantum algorithms might exploit energy level transitions, making quantum computers perform specific tasks exponentially faster than classical computers.

While the ladder of quantized energy might appear as mere steps, they are foundational in the world of quantum computing. They provide the discrete scaffold on which the fascinating and often counterintuitive realm of quantum mechanics rests and where the magic of quantum computing begins to shine. So, as we dive deeper into quantum computers, remember that these discrete energy levels play an instrumental role, choreographing the dance of qubits.

## A Dramatic Shift in Understanding

Quantum mechanics challenges classical deterministic laws and introduces probabilistic behavior at the microscopic level. At the heart of this divergence is how these two branches of physics treat matter and energy.

## The Classical

*Predictability and Determinism*

In the realm of classical physics, which governs most of our everyday experiences, the world behaves in a deterministic way. If we throw a ball upwards, classical physics lets us calculate, with a high degree of accuracy, when and where it will land. The same goes for other physical systems; we can predict their future states if we know the current state and the forces acting upon them. This predictability comes from the deterministic nature of classical laws—Newton's laws of motion or Maxwell's equations, for instance.

## Entering Quantum

*A World of Probabilities*

However, when we zoom into the atomic and subatomic scales, classical rules begin to break down. Here, the world operates not on strict determinism but on probabilities. Particles like electrons don't have definite positions or velocities but exist in a superposition of many possibilities until they are measured. It's not just about tiny particles behaving oddly; it's a profound shift in understanding that challenges our intuitions.

The wave-particle duality we touched on earlier is a cornerstone of this. Electrons can behave both as particles and waves. Unlike a classical object, which is either a wave (like a sound wave) or a particle (like a football), quantum entities defy such categorization.

*The Heartbeat of Quantum Computing*

So, how does all this feed into quantum computing? The reason quantum computers can process vast amounts of data simultaneously isn't magic—it's quantum mechanics in action.

Remember the principle of superposition? That's the ultimate quantum idea. In classical computers, a bit is either a 0 or a 1. But a qubit, governed by quantum rules, can exist in both states, allowing quantum computers to process multiple possibilities at once.

Entanglement, another inherently quantum phenomenon, lets qubits become interconnected in ways that classical bits never can. This lets quantum computers execute complex algorithms that rely on these entangled states, tackling problems classical computers would take millennia to solve.

Moreover, the probabilistic behavior of quantum systems, which might seem like a hurdle at first, becomes an advantage in quantum computing. Particular computational tasks, like optimization problems, are inherently probabilistic, and the quantum computers' nature is tailor-made to handle them.

In the vast tapestry of the universe, classical physics paints the broad strokes, the mountains, rivers, and forests. But quantum mechanics fills in the intricate details—the delicate patterns on a butterfly's wing or the fleeting shimmer of a dewdrop at dawn. As we push the boundaries of computation, these traits, these quantum characteristics, grant quantum computers immense power. So, as you ponder over the marvel of quantum computing, remember: its heart beats in quantum time, dancing to the rhythm of a universe more intricate and wondrous than classical eyes can see.

## Quantum Measurements and the Role of Observables

*Navigating the Quantum Terrain*

Picture yourself as an intrepid explorer on the vast quantum continent. This realm is unlike any you've ever traversed. With every step, the landscape shivers with possibilities. In your hand, you hold a unique compass, capable of indicating not just North and South but also a blend of "quantum North" and "quantum South". This peculiar behavior represents our qubit. Thanks to the wonders of superposition, it can point simultaneously in both directions. But, when the moment comes to commit – when you decide your path forward – the compass decisively chooses one direction. This mirrors the action of a qubit: remaining in superposition until measured, at which point it locks into a definite state.

*The Quantum State and Its Observation*

In classical mechanics, if you have a spinning top, you can easily measure its position and momentum without any hiccups. The act of measuring doesn't change the properties of the system. However, quantum mechanics throws us a curveball.

As you might recall from our earlier discussions, a qubit exists in a superposition of states until measured. This doesn't mean the qubit is simultaneously in all possible states; rather, it's in a state that is a combination of these possibilities. Imagine being on the Quantum

Continent and standing at a crossroad without a clear path marked; the qubit's actual position remains unknown until you decide to check.

When you measure a qubit, you force it into one of its possible states. The qubit will then "collapse" into either a $|0\rangle$ state or a $|1\rangle$ state. The intriguing bit is that, until the measurement, you cannot predict with certainty which state it will end up in.

## Peering into the Quantum Realm

*Observables*

In the world of quantum mechanics, when we talk about measuring, we're discussing observables. Observables are specific properties of the quantum system that can be measured. They are represented by operators (mathematical entities) that act upon the quantum state (or the wave function) to provide a specific outcome.

Consider the act of measuring the spin of an electron in a magnetic field. The electron's spin might be either in alignment with the field, known as a spin-up state, or opposite to the field, known as a spin-down state. These two possible outcomes are the observables for the electron's spin.

However, here's where the Quantum Continent's mysterious terrain shows its peculiar nature. If you were to measure the spin of an electron that is in a superposition of both spin-up and spin-down states, quantum mechanics won't provide a deterministic answer. Instead, you'll get probabilities. The electron might be 70% likely to be in a spin-up state and 30% in a spin-down state. The exact outcome is revealed only upon measurement.

## Interacting with Qubits

*A Glimpse of the Quantum Lab*

How do scientists actually "see" or interact with qubits, you wonder? Let's get a visual. While we can't "see" qubits like we see objects in our daily lives, scientists employ sophisticated equipment to interact with them. Consider a quantum lab like a master control room filled with specialized machinery. Devices cooled to near absolute zero to create an environment where quantum effects dominate. Lasers and microwave pulses are shot at specific particles, like electrons in a magnetic field or ions suspended in traps, to manipulate and measure their states.

In the case of superconducting qubits, often used in quantum computers, the qubits are tiny circuits made out of superconducting materials. When these materials are supercooled, they allow current to flow without resistance. The flow of electrons in these circuits, combined with magnetic fields, produces quantized energy levels. Through precision control and measurement equipment, scientists can manipulate the states of these qubits and measure their properties.

Quantum measurement and observables guide us through the process of extracting information from a quantum system. While the Quantum Continent's landscapes may seem unpredictable and mysterious, the principles of quantum mechanics, paired with cutting-edge technology, provide the tools to navigate and understand quantum, bringing the promise and potential of quantum computing ever closer to our grasp.

## Quantum Operators and Gates

*Navigating the Quantum Landscape*

In our vast quantum continent, the familiar tools of maps, compass adjustments, and traversing techniques become analogs to what scientists use in the quantum world: operators and gates.

To better understand, let's build upon our analogy. In regular exploration, if you want to reach a specific destination, you might need to adjust your compass's calibration or decide on an exact route. Quantum operators and gates perform a similar function. They help "calibrate" or "navigate" our qubits to desired quantum states or to perform specific quantum tasks.

- Quantum Operators: Think of these as compass calibrations. They act on quantum states, transforming them from one to another. Essentially, they represent the different interactions a quantum system can have. If you've ever adjusted a compass for a magnetic declination or noted prominent landmarks, you've conceptually used an 'operator' to modify your understanding of direction.

- Quantum Gates: Analogous to pathways or routes in regular terrain, quantum gates guide qubits through specific transformations. When a qubit passes through a gate, it undergoes a distinct change in its state, just as traversing a mountain path might take you to a new altitude. There's a rich variety of these gates, each executing a distinct operation and uniquely guiding our quantum journey.

In the quantum continent, instead of trekking mountains or crossing rivers, scientists guide qubits through specific sequences of gates, tweaking and calibrating them with operators, aiming to get them to a specific state or execute a particular quantum algorithm.

## Quantum Measurements and Observables

*Numerical Navigators*

Now that we have our qubit adjusted and on the desired path, how do we know where it stands? Here is where the climax of our quantum expedition takes place: measurements and observables.

Imagine you're equipped with a multi-functional gadget while exploring – let's call it a Quantum Swiss Army Knife. This isn't an ordinary knife; instead, each tool within it represents a different observable. Just as the blade, corkscrew, or screwdriver in a traditional Swiss Army knife has a specific function, each observable in our quantum knife is designed to measure a unique property of our quantum entities, like position, spin, or energy.

These observables are the mathematical "tools" that scientists deploy to extract information from quantum systems. They're not tangible instruments in the usual sense, but mathematical frameworks or operations. When applied to a quantum entity, such as an electron, an observable predicts the potential outcome of a specific measurement, like the electron's position or spin orientation.

These "observables" are scientists' best friends in the quantum realm. Remember, these tools are primarily mathematical methods. They let scientists predict and understand how quantum systems behave. However, tangible instruments await us in Chapter 2 when we move from the theoretical world to the experimental labs. Tools like the Stern–Gerlach apparatus or spectrometers are essential for observing and measuring quantum properties. But more on that when we discuss the architecture of quantum computers!

In quantum computing, understanding these mathematical observables is as pivotal as a traveler knowing how to utilize each tool in their Swiss Army knife. Just as each instrument in the knife is vital for specific tasks in an expedition, harnessing the nuances of these quantum observables is fundamental for navigating and extracting valuable information in the quantum computing world.

## Interpreting Eigen's Value

*Eigenvalues and Eigenstates*

The word "eigen" is German for "characteristic" or "own." In quantum mechanics, "eigen" refers to characteristic properties that belong inherently to something. In mathematics, especially linear algebra, eigenvalues and eigenvectors (or eigenstates in quantum mechanics) arise when considering linear transformations. Essentially, they highlight the most "characteristic" behaviors of that transformation.

So, "eigen" isn't a tool or process per se, but rather a descriptor. When we say "eigenvalue" or "eigenstate," we're talking about characteristic values or states of a system. In quantum mechanics, the eigenstates represent the possible states in which a quantum system can be found when measured, and the eigenvalues are the possible outcomes or readings of that measurement.

Essentially, eigenvalues and eigenstates help describe quantum systems' inherent characteristic behaviors. They're fundamental to understanding how quantum systems evolve and how measurements yield specific outcomes.

To venture deeper into our quantum journey, imagine standing atop a cliff, looking out across our expansive quantum landscape. You notice particular points or peaks that stand out. In quantum mechanics, these prominent points resemble *eigenstates* — specific, well-defined states where a quantum system can exist.

Consider our trusty compass. As we've used it to traverse the quantum landscape, it has points where it settles naturally, giving a clear, precise reading. In quantum lingo, when we measure a quantum system in an eigenstate, we receive a precise outcome termed an *eigenvalue.* This eigenvalue is the "reading" or value associated with that particular eigenstate.

Let's relate this to something more familiar. In the world of music, think of a guitar string. When plucked, it vibrates and produces a sound. This sound is most intense and clear at particular frequencies. These frequencies are like the eigenvalues, and the specific vibration patterns at these frequencies can be considered eigenstates. Similarly, in the quantum world, particles or systems exhibit distinct characteristic vibrations or states (eigenstates) that correspond to specific outcomes or values (eigenvalues) when measured.

Why is this concept crucial for quantum computers? Scientists and physicists play around with these eigenstates to perform computations when processing information. They manipulate qubits to exist in particular eigenstates that, when measured, provide us with the desired outcomes, or eigenvalues. Understanding eigenstates and eigenvalues is like understanding the language or signs of this foreign land, ensuring that we can interpret and manipulate the quantum landscape effectively.

## The Uncertainty Principle

*Nature's Boundary on Precision*

As we travel deeper into the quantum wilderness, a fundamental principle confronts our intuitive understanding of the world: the Heisenberg Uncertainty Principle. Imagine standing at the base of a steep cliff, looking up, and knowing there's a limit to how high you can see clearly without specialized tools. In our quantum exploration, the Uncertainty Principle is that imposing cliff, reminding us that nature sets certain boundaries even in this precise domain.

*Heisenberg's Startling Revelation*

Werner Heisenberg, a titan of quantum mechanics, unveiled a fascinating truth about the quantum world in 1927. He said there's a rule in the world of tiny particles: The more precisely we know a particle's position, the less precisely we can know its momentum (mass multiplied by its velocity), and vice versa. It's a fundamental quirk of the quantum world, where some things just can't be precisely known at the same time.

## Implications for Measurement Outcomes

In our quantum expedition, this means that our quantum compass – no matter how advanced or precise – will always have a degree of uncertainty when reading pairs of coordinates simultaneously. In the context of quantum computing, this is a game-changer. If classical bits are like clear signposts on a well-trodden path, qubits, with their built-in uncertainty, are like the shifting sands of a desert, changing their nature the moment we try to observe them too closely.

But why does nature impose this restriction? While the exact reason remains one of the profound mysteries of quantum mechanics, some physicists suggest that it's a consequence of the wave nature of particles. Others view it as a result of the fundamental constraints of the universe itself.

One thing is for sure. This principle doesn't arise from our inadequacies in measurement tools or techniques. It's a fundamental aspect of nature, embedded deep within the fabric of the universe.

## A Gift in Disguise?

At first glance, the Uncertainty Principle might seem like a frustrating constraint; but in the realm of quantum computing, it's something of a double-edged sword. While it introduces challenges, it also opens up a world of possibilities. The probabilistic nature of qubits arises from this principle, which enables quantum computers to process vast amounts of information at once, making them far more powerful than their classical counterparts for specific tasks.

While the Uncertainty Principle reminds us of nature's boundaries, it also proves the vast potential and intrigue of the quantum field. As we gear up to make sense of quantum computing, we must understand and respect these boundaries while harnessing the opportunities they offer.

## Time Complexity

*A Glimpse into the Quantum Clock*

As we progress across the quantum continent, imagine we're setting out on specific trails – these trails represent algorithms. Now, just as one might take a direct route through a forest because it's the quickest way to a destination, we often choose algorithms based on their efficiency.

At the heart of evaluating this efficiency is a concept called **time complexity**. Think of it as a measure of the pace at which we can traverse these quantum trails. Specifically, time complexity refers to the efficiency of algorithms with respect to the size of their inputs. In simple terms, it's a measure of how an algorithm's running time (or sometimes the space used) grows as the size of the input grows.

But here's where the quantum landscape showcases its unique terrain: Quantum algorithms can, in certain instances, traverse these trails faster than classical computers. Thanks to principles like superposition and entanglement, they can process vast amounts of information at once. This enables them to solve problems in fewer steps.

However, remember, the quantum realm is filled with nuances. While quantum algorithms can offer speed-ups for specific problems, they aren't universally faster. Chapter 4 promises a treasure of algorithm gems. As we further navigate this quantum land, understanding time complexity helps us gauge the potential of quantum computers in reshaping computational horizons.

## Bits vs. Qubits - A Tale of Two Computations

*Quantum Computing with Classical Computing*

Meet the classical bit and the quantum qubit: two players on the computational stage. One is the tried-and-true backbone of every device you've ever used; its language is binary, straightforward—zeros and ones. The other? A trailblazing headliner capable of quantum superposition and rewriting the rules of what's possible in computing. Prepare to witness a duel of traditions vs. innovations as a new challenger faces the classical champion in the information arena.

**Visual/Table 1**: Hardware

| Aspect | Classical Computing | Quantum Computing |
|---|---|---|
| Fundamental Unit | Bit (0 or 1) | Qubit (0, 1, or superposition) |
| Storage | Transistors | Quantum gates, particles like electrons, photons |
| Operations | Logical gates (AND, OR, NOT) | Quantum gates (Hadamard, Pauli-X, etc.) |

*Visual/Table 1: Basic Architectural Difference - Bits vs. Qubits*

## Classical Computers (Bits)

- **Nature:** Deterministic

- **State:** 0 OR 1

- Information Processing: Sequential

- **Primary Mechanism:** Electric current represents 0 or 1

## Quantum Computers (Qubits)

- **Nature:** Probabilistic

- **State:** 0 AND 1 (Superposition)

- Information Processing: Parallel

- **Primary Mechanism:** Quantum state of a particle (e.g., electron's spin)

*Classical Computers*

At the heart of every classical computer is the binary system, where information is represented using bits that can be either 0 or 1. Think of them as light switches: they are either off (0) or on (1). The computations in classical computers are predominantly sequential, meaning tasks are processed one after the other. The physical manifestation of a bit in hardware typically relies on electrical currents. When a current flows, the bit is '1'; when there's no current, it's 0'.

*Quantum Computers*

Quantum computers revolutionize this foundational concept. Instead of bits, they use qubits. Imagine you have a spinning top instead of a simple light switch. This top can spin clockwise (0), counter-clockwise (1), or any state in between, representing the principle of superposition, where qubits exist in a state of 0, 1, or both. This unique trait allows quantum computers to process information in parallel. Multiple tasks or calculations can be tackled at once, making them much more powerful. The manifestation of a qubit isn't through electric current; instead, it is often through a particle's quantum state, like an electron's spin. This probabilistic nature allows quantum computers to explore multiple solutions and why they're so groundbreaking in computing.

While a classical explorer has to check one path at a time in the vast continent, a quantum explorer can tread numerous paths, increasing the chances of finding treasures (or solutions) much more efficiently.

By understanding this foundational difference in architecture, one can begin to grasp the transformative potential that quantum computers bring to the table.

**Visual/Table 2**: Computation

| Aspect | Classical Computing | Quantum Computing |
|---|---|---|
| Processing | Deterministic | Probabilistic |
| Parallelism | Limited (typically managed with multi-threading) | Inherent (through superposition) |
| Optimization | Often NP-hard problems remain unsolvable | Some problems solvable in polynomial time (e.g., Shor's algorithm for factoring) |

*Visual/Table 2: Problem-Solving Capacity - Linear vs. Exponential*

## Classical Computers

- **Problem Scaling:** Linear (For many complex problems)

- **Speed:** Fast for everyday tasks, slower for computationally intensive tasks

- **Limitation:** Exponentially increasing time with complex problems (e.g., factorizing large numbers)

# Quantum Computers

- **Problem Scaling:** Exponential (For specific problems)

- **Speed:** Potentially much faster for specific computationally intensive tasks

- **Advantage:** Can solve certain problems in polynomial time, which classical computers solve in exponential time (e.g., quantum factorization)

*Classical Computers*

In traditional computing, as problems grow in complexity, the time it takes for them to be solved often increases in a straightforward manner. Imagine processing 10 units of data in 10 minutes. If it scales linearly, 20 units would take 20 minutes, and 30 units would take 30 minutes. It's predictable, much like searching through a small box of items one by one.

However, classical computers face a significantly steeper challenge for some complex issues. The time required can shoot up exponentially. This is like trying to find a needle in a haystack. Every time the haystack doubles in size, the time it takes to search can also double. While this linear and predictable increase might be manageable for smaller haystacks (or simpler problems), searching becomes a monumental task as the haystacks expand. While classical computers excel at many of our day-to-day tasks, they falter when faced with factorizing massive numbers — tasks that could take years, decades, or even longer to complete.

*Quantum Computers*

Now, enter the world of quantum computing. For specific problems, quantum computers don't just incrementally improve the speed; they change the scale of problem-solving altogether. Returning to our haystack analogy, imagine if, instead of searching straw by straw, you had a magical tool that could probe half the haystack at once, then a quarter, and so on. This is an oversimplified representation of the exponential advantage of quantum computers. For tasks they are tailored to, such as quantum factorization, they can solve problems in polynomial time. Simply, the relationship between the size of a problem and the number of steps (or "time") it takes to solve it. A feat unimaginable for classical machines dealing with the same issue.

In our Quantum Continent, a classical explorer might comb through methodically, one region after another, the quantum explorer can rapidly zoom into areas of interest, making discoveries at a pace the classical explorer could only dream of.

This potential for exponential problem-solving showcases quantum computers' vast, transformative potential, especially for problems that have long been deemed unsolvable within reasonable timeframes by classical standards.

**Visual/Table 3**: Information

| Aspect | Classical Computing | Quantum Computing |
|--------|---------------------|-------------------|
| Encoding | Binary | Superposition, entanglement |
| Retrieval | Direct from memory | Quantum measurement, collapse of wave function |

*Visual/Table 3: Quantum Entanglement - The Deep Bond of Qubits*

## Classical Computers

- **Interrelation:** Bits operate independently.

- **Information Exchange:** Direct and separate pathways.

- **Effect:** No change in one bit's state can affect another's.

## Quantum Computers

- **Interrelation:** Qubits can be deeply entangled.

- **Information Exchange:** Instantaneous correlation, regardless of distance.

- **Effect:** State change in one qubit can immediately affect the state of another entangled qubit.

## Classical Computers

Imagine classical bits as individual light switches in a room. Each switch operates independently; turning one on or off doesn't affect the others. The flow of information between bits is clear-cut and precise, much like two people passing notes to each other. While these switches (or bits) are incredibly efficient at rapidly flicking on and off, representing vast amounts of digital data, they cannot blend or entangle their states. This independence makes their operations lightning-fast and reliable for most tasks we use computers for today, but it also sets boundaries on the types of complex computations they can handle.

## Quantum Computers

Imagine two tuning forks placed in separate rooms of a vast mansion. When one is struck and begins to resonate, the other instantly vibrates at the same frequency, regardless of the walls and distances separating them. This harmonious connection is defined as 'quantum entanglement.' Qubits, once they enter this synchronized resonance, form a deep bond. A vibration in one qubit can instantly reverberate in its entangled partner, even if they're situated in distant wings of the mansion. This isn't just acoustic harmony; it's an immediate, profound connection, surpassing any classical understanding of sound or resonance. With unparalleled proficiency, quantum computers leverage this unique quality of qubits and address problems with interlinked data points.

In our exploration analogy, while a classical explorer would set up individual communication channels with each team member, ensuring messages are relayed one at a time, a quantum explorer possesses a magical walkie-talkie. With this device, when one team member discovers something, others instantly gain insights, even if they're miles apart, enhancing their collective understanding of the landscape.

Entanglement represents one of the most groundbreaking and mysterious facets of quantum mechanics, propelling quantum computers into a realm of computation that classical machines can't access.

Contrasting quantum directly with classical systems can sharpen our understanding. This distinction isn't merely in the 'hardware'; but also in how they process information. We now understand that 'quantum' doesn't equate to 'better.' It signifies 'different.' While quantum computers excel in certain areas, classical machines remain irreplaceable in others. This knowledge will be our compass as we navigate the quantum domain, highlighting where quantum truly offers a unique advantage.

## Superposition

*The Quantum Dance of Possibilities*

Imagine a forest where every single tree showcases the vibrant green leaves of summer, the golden hues of autumn, the bare branches of winter, and the budding blossoms of spring. Each tree embodies all seasons at any given moment, not committing to just one. However, the moment you decide to capture a photograph of an individual tree, it chooses a single season to display, as if it had been in that state all along. This magical forest is much like the world of qubits in a superposition state: existing in multiple possibilities at once, but choosing a definite state only upon observation.

This phenomenon is not just a quirk or an abstract idea. It's anchored deeply in the very fabric of quantum mechanics. Quantum entities, like electrons, don't commit to a particular state until observed. They dance among the realm of possibilities until a conscious observer decides to measure them. When measured, these quantum entities collapse to a single, definitive state.

The true power of superposition becomes even more evident when considering its computational implications. When a qubit is in superposition, it can process information as if it were jointly in the 0 and 1 states. Think back to our forest. If each tree represents a qubit, then a forest with two trees (or two qubits) can collectively represent four seasons or states (00, 01, 10, 11). What about a forest with three trees? That's eight simultaneous states. With every additional qubit, the number of possibilities or superposed states doubles. This exponential expansion allows quantum computers to explore vast computational paths in a single command.

Now, you might wonder, why does nature allow this? The exact 'why' remains one of the profound mysteries of quantum mechanics. But what's clear is that this ability is anchored in the very nature of the quantum world. Quantum systems, by their intrinsic properties, defy our classical intuitions. They dance in a realm of probabilities until a specific observation forces them into a definite state, much like the trees of our enchanted forest choosing a season upon the click of a camera. This behavior offers quantum computers the potential to solve problems deemed impossible for classical machines, showcasing quantum's incredible power and magic.

## Entanglement: Quantum Ties that Bind

In quantum, there's a phenomenon that even Einstein once labeled as "spooky action at a distance." Entanglement is undoubtedly one of the most mystifying yet fundamental principles of quantum mechanics.

Imagine standing in a vast forest filled with countless trees in various states, just as we've discussed. Suppose two trees, let's say an oak and a pine, form a unique bond so special that even if these trees were uprooted and planted on opposite sides of the world, they would remain interconnected. By some magical connection, if the oak tree suddenly sheds its leaves in autumn, the pine tree will also change, perhaps by dropping its needles, even if pines don't naturally do so.

This kind of inexplicable linkage is what happens between entangled qubits. Once entangled, the state of one qubit directly relates to the state of the other, regardless of the distance between them. Altering the state of one instantly affects the other, transcending our classical understanding of information transfer.

*Why does entanglement matter to quantum computers?* Entanglement allows quantum computers to perform complex operations involving multiple qubits simultaneously. Because these qubits are interlinked, operations on one immediately impact the other, leading to highly synchronized computation.

In the context of quantum computation, entangled qubits allow quantum computers to explore multiple solutions in a coordinated fashion. This "quantum teamwork" enables quantum computers to solve problems like factoring large numbers and processing complex interrelated data.

In a real-world analogy, consider two interlinked traffic systems in different cities. If the traffic flow on the east side of a city suddenly changes—say, a major road is closed—the entire city's system instantaneously adapts, redirecting traffic to maintain optimal flow without any visible communication. The power quantum entanglement brings to computation is performance and adaptability in processing complex scenarios promptly.

## Quantum Tunneling: Navigating the Energy Landscape

Imagine hiking through a vast mountainous landscape, searching for the lowest valley—the perfect campsite. Sometimes, you find a spot that seems perfect, but then you realize there are even lower valleys beyond the next ridge. The problem is that climbing over each one to check the adjacent valley can be tiring and time-consuming. Now, imagine if you had a magical ability to just "phase" right through the hill to see what's on the other side without all the effort of climbing. This, in essence, is quantum tunneling.

1. **The Quantum Energy Landscape**: Quantum systems, like our hypothetical hiking terrain, possess an energy landscape, which consists of various states with differing energy levels. Some states are

nestled in deep valleys (low energy), while others are perched atop hills (high energy).

2.   **The Challenge of Local Minima**: In many computational problems, particularly optimization, the objective is to find this deepest valley, representing the optimal solution. However, it's easy for a system to get trapped in a small dip, mistaking it for the lowest point. This is known as a local minimum.

3.   **Tunneling to the Rescue**: This is where quantum tunneling becomes pivotal. Instead of being confined to the small dip, quantum systems have the uncanny ability to "tunnel" right through the hill, probing the landscape beyond without scaling the peak. In more technical terms, qubits can bypass energy barriers, allowing them to explore states that might be energetically off-limits in a classical scenario.

Such a mechanism is invaluable in quantum computations, especially quantum annealing processes. By tunneling through barriers, quantum systems can efficiently escape suboptimal local minima, enhancing the likelihood of discovering the true optimal solution. This feature embodies the strange beauty of quantum mechanics and accentuates the unparalleled computational potential of quantum computers.

# Spin

*The Quantum Gyroscope*

Every particle in the quantum realm comes with its own set of characteristics, akin to humans having unique fingerprints. One of these distinguishing features, which remains intrinsic to particles like electrons, is the property of *spin.*

## Intrinsic Nature of Spin

Unlike our typical understanding of spinning, where an object physically rotates around an axis (like Earth around its axis), the spin of a quantum particle doesn't describe an actual rotation. Instead, it's an intrinsic form of angular momentum. Picture an ice skater spinning with her arms outstretched. As she pulls her arms in, she spins faster. This change in her rotation speed corresponds to angular momentum. Quantum particles possess similar momentum, but not because they are "spinning" like a top. It's a fundamental property they just inherently have.

## Angular Momentum at Play

Classically, angular momentum is visualized as the quantity of rotation an object has, considering its mass and shape. In the quantum world, however, particles like electrons have spin angular momenta that are quantized, meaning they can take on only specific values. For electrons, these values are often called "spin-up" and "spin-down." Much like the quantum leaps of electrons between energy levels, this quantization adds another layer of mystery to the already tricky quantum world.

## Relevance to Wave-Particle Duality

Earlier, we explored the intriguing nature of wave-particle duality, where particles like electrons exhibit wave-like and particle-like properties. Spin plays a role here too. It becomes particularly evident when we study phenomena like the Stern-Gerlach experiment. Our particles with spin are subjected to magnetic fields; they exhibit quantized angular momenta, aligning in particular directions, reinforcing the idea that quantum properties, like spin, relate closely to the dual nature of particles.

Spin, as covered here, provides a foundation for understanding many quantum phenomena and operations, especially when we venture into quantum computing architecture and operations in the following chapters.

## Bell's Inequality and the Deep Mysteries of Entanglement

*The EPR Paradox: Quantum Spookiness and Computing at a Distance*

In the vast forest of quantum possibilities, intertwined trees represent entangled qubits - the fundamental building blocks of quantum computers. Einstein, Podolsky, and Rosen (EPR) were the first to delve deep into this mysterious quantum forest. In 1935, they proposed a challenging scenario. Imagine two qubits that once interacted and are now separated across a quantum chip or even across vast physical distances. Measuring one would instantaneously determine the state of the other. Einstein termed this "spooky action at a distance," hoping for some hidden variables to explain this in line with classical logic.

## Bell's Inequality

*The Litmus Test for Quantum Computers*

In the 1960s, John Bell proposed a method to determine the nature of these intertwined qubits. His test, known as Bell's Inequality, checks whether qubit connections are genuinely 'quantum' or can be explained through hidden variables. Quantum computers thrive in this environment, leveraging the 'spooky' entangled states to simultaneously process vast amounts of information. Real-world experiments on quantum systems, acting as preliminary quantum computers, defy classical logic, suggesting they operate in a profoundly non-local dimension.

## Local Realism vs. Quantum Computing Power

"Local realism" is akin to processors communicating via set pathways. In the quantum system, entangled qubits don't follow these rules. They communicate, or rather share connectivity, in a non-local fashion, making quantum computers incredibly powerful. This non-locality, tapped into by quantum algorithms, is a game-changer, ushering in an era where quantum machines teach us the boundaries of possibility.

## From Sci-Fi to Quantum Reality

In the world of quantum computing, teleportation and superdense coding aren't just science fiction; they're foundational techniques. Quantum teleportation allows the state of one qubit to be recreated in another distant qubit, a potential cornerstone for quantum communication networks. Meanwhile, superdense coding maximizes the information transmitted between qubits, promising efficiency levels never before achieved.

## Bell, Qubits, and the Quantum Computing Revolution

Bell's theorem and the experiments inspired by it have a direct bearing on our understanding and development of quantum computers. Entangled qubits, like our forest's intertwined trees, operate in a world that classical logic can't easily grasp. By appreciating the counterintuitive nature of qubits and their entangled states, we're poised to harness the immense power and potential of quantum computing.

Chapter 1 has unveiled the magical world of quantum physics, drawing us into its whirlwind of wonders and phenomena. Now, with a grasp of these foundational principles, Chapter 2 promises a thrilling exploration into the architectural marvels of quantum computers. From the energetic terrain of abstract theories to the tangible, cutting-edge machinery, our quest is about to take an exhilarating turn. Let's explore the blueprints and building blocks of this revolutionary technology.

# CHAPTER 2

## BUILDING QUANTUM COMPUTERS

### The Quantum Foundation

Before we look at quantum computers in action, it's pivotal to grasp its foundational concept. Quantum originates from the Latin "quantus," which means "how much." That's not simply a matter of language but a window into a profound shift in our understanding of the universe.

In the early 20th century, scientists realized that energy, at its most fundamental level, doesn't flow in a smooth, continuous stream. Instead, it exists in discrete packets or "quanta." These discrete packets of energy form the very bedrock of quantum mechanics. This revelation is like a flowing river, which, when examined, contains individual water droplets.

When we discuss building a quantum computer, we're essentially addressing the art of harnessing these quanta—these discrete energy units—to process information. Unlike the classical bits in traditional computers, quantum bits, or qubits, capitalize on the principles of superposition, allowing them to hold vast amounts of information and process extensive datasets simultaneously.

Economic considerations add another layer to this intricate dance. Questions arise: What's the financial outlay for building and maintaining each quantum computer? How power-intensive is each method? And how prevalent is each technology in the current landscape? Asking such questions lays the foundation and our promise to make quantum computing for everyone.

The fragility of quantum computations cannot be overstated. Quantum systems are like delicate instruments, vulnerable to external influences such as temperature variations, electrical fluctuations, and even cosmic interference. This sensitivity underscores the need for quantum error correction, our safeguard against such 'noises,' ensuring reliability and accuracy.

You're about to uncover how the 'quantum' principle paves the way for an unprecedented leap in computational expertise.

## Quantum Computing Architecture

In our quest to construct the intricate highways of quantum computing, we first must understand the diverse landscapes these roads can traverse. Just as ancient builders had the choice of cobblestone, dirt, or brick for their streets, modern quantum architects have a range of foundational materials and methods at their disposal. But these are no ordinary roads; they are highways to a future full of computational wonders.

*Emphasizing Quantum Mechanics' Role in Quantum Computing*

Imagine for a moment the blueprint of an architectural wonder: a monumental bridge that spans a river. In classical engineering, this bridge would have supports at exact intervals, and its design would adhere strictly to the well-established laws of physics and materials science. The predictability of these laws ensures the safety and stability of the bridge, allowing it to bear the weight of vehicles and withstand environmental challenges.

In the quantum realm, however, the blueprint undergoes a dramatic transformation. The bridge, once limited by classical constraints, can now exist in multiple configurations simultaneously, and its supports can be both present and absent at the same time. This bewildering phenomenon is not a whim of a foolish architect but the tangible influence of quantum mechanics on design and construction.

The foundational principles of quantum mechanics – superposition, entanglement, and quantum interference – are not just theoretical curiosities. They empower quantum computers with capabilities far beyond their classical counterparts. These principles don't modify the blueprint; they expand our possibilities, allowing quantum architects to explore innovative and uncharted designs.

But why is quantum mechanics so pivotal in this context? Classical computers, built on bits, function within the rigid confines of binary states. Qubits, however, can perform superposition. This dual-state existence grants quantum computers a computational bandwidth that classical systems can't match. Picture our bridge again, but instead of simply connecting two landmasses, it interlinks multiple destinations, offering countless pathways and outcomes.

Harnessing the principles of quantum mechanics is not merely an academic exercise—it's the foundation for constructing quantum computers. Architects, engineers, and physicists actively design tools to tap directly into the quantum traits. Every component, every device, every meticulously crafted piece is a tangible manifestation of quantum principles.

As we continue mapping out these quantum highways, remember that each path, gate, and junction is directly associated with the quantum phenomena. This isn't just about conceptual understanding; it's about physically chiseling into the quantum landscape, molding it into computational marvels. Let's continue exploring the tools and structures we build to unlock its potential.

## Components of Quantum Computers

To understand the architecture of a quantum computer, let's visualize it as a sprawling, sophisticated highway system. Just as our modern highways aren't merely tar slapped onto earth but consist of multiple layers, from a foundational bedrock to the surface layer, quantum computers are built upon several layers, each having its own role and complexity. At the heart of this quantum highway system are the lanes—the qubits.

*Quantum Bits (Qubits)*

Much like highway lanes carry cars, trucks, and buses, the qubits in a quantum computer carry quantum information. Suppose classical bits in traditional computers are akin to one-lane roads that only allow a car to go in one direction at a time (0 or 1). In that case, qubits can be imagined as multi-layered highways where vehicles can float between layers, moving in many directions simultaneously, thanks to quantum superposition. This 'floating' car isn't committed to one layer or direction but exists in a state that's a combination of all possible states, a feature unique to our quantum highway.

While our analogy likens qubits to multi-layered highways, it's important to understand that qubits are tangible and physically real, albeit operating under principles that can seem almost mystical. Magnetic or electrical fields and lasers are just a few tools we use to interact with qubits.

*Quantum Gates and Operations*

Building onto our highway analogy, let's consider quantum gates and operations. Think of gates as the traffic signals and junctions of our quantum highway, directing the flow of our quantum cars — the qubits. Much like how traffic signals dictate vehicle movement, these gates control qubit behavior, ensuring they operate in specific, desired ways.

It's essential to understand that while quantum gates are conceptualized abstractly, similar to logic gates in classical computing, their real-world counterparts are physical entities. They come to life through controlled interactions among qubits. The physical system in which the qubits operate determines how these interactions are achieved. Thus, quantum gates possess both an algorithmic representation and a tangible manifestation.

*Constructing Operators*

Diving a little deeper into the intricacies, these operators are the set of instructions governing the operations on our quantum highway. Unary operators, for instance, can be visualized as instructions for a single lane, binary for junctions involving two lanes, and ternary for complex three-way intersections. They dictate how our quantum vehicles (qubits) interact, merge, or diverge.

But beyond this conceptual layer, these operators don't exist in isolation from the hardware. When implementing an operator on a quantum computer, we often use precise sequences of laser pulses or finely tuned electromagnetic fields. For instance, to make two qubits interact in a particular way (binary operation), a specific frequency of light might be shone on them. This light manipulates the qubits into a state where they can effectively "talk" to each other, achieving the desired operation. It's a dance of precision, where the choreography of mathematical operators is brought to life through the artistry of physical interaction.

*Quantum Circuit Design*

A quantum circuit is the equivalent of a planned roadway system. Just as city planners design roads, intersections, and highways to optimize traffic flow, quantum circuits are meticulously designed to perform specific tasks or computations. The layout of these circuits is crucial. Much like an inefficiently planned road can lead to traffic jams, an improperly designed quantum circuit can result in computational inefficiencies.

Constructing these circuits is an intricate ballet of precision and control. Here's how we capture the essence of quantum circuits in practice:

- **Positioning Qubits**: Qubits need to be placed with pinpoint precision. In labs, this is achieved using cryogenic chambers, where temperatures plunge close to absolute zero, offering a stable environment for qubits, especially for certain types like superconducting qubits.

- **Gating & Interactions**: Every gate in the quantum circuit translates into very specific and controlled interactions among qubits. The kind of interaction depends on the type of qubit and the operation:

- **Laser Beams**: Finely tuned lasers manipulate individual ions in systems with trapped ions as qubits. By targeting an ion with a laser pulse, scientists can adjust its energy state or make it interact with a neighboring ion.

- **Electrical Pulses**: Short bursts of controlled electrical pulses help manipulate the qubit states and interactions for superconducting qubits. These pulses are delivered through meticulously designed circuitry, ensuring precision.

- **Magnetic Resonance**: In some cases, like Nuclear Magnetic Resonance (NMR) quantum computers, magnetic fields are applied to influence the spin states of nuclei, effectively creating quantum gates.

At the intersection of advanced technology and quantum theory, researchers and engineers use these tools to bring quantum circuits from theory to reality, making the promises of quantum computation obtainable.

*Photonic*

Envisioning our quantum highway, photonic quantum systems can be seen as super-speed trains or light-rails. Unlike the traditional vehicles that operate on roads, these special "trains" run on tracks of light. Photons—particles of light—serve as the quantum counterpart to the vehicles, traversing vast distances at breathtaking speeds. In quantum computing, their unique properties make them a prized choice for certain architectures.

In the laboratory setting, creating and manipulating photonic qubits requires a symphony of high-tech apparatus:

- **Optical Tables**: These specially designed tables minimize vibrations and ensure stability. Every piece of equipment put on these tables, from lasers to beam splitters, stays rock-steady, ensuring precision.

- **Lasers**: To generate individual photons or pairs of entangled photons, specific types of lasers are used. The light's color (or wavelength) and pulse duration can be carefully controlled to produce the desired photonic states.

- **Beam Splitters & Mirrors**: These are used to direct the path of photons. Much like how traffic lights guide vehicles on roads, beam splitters and mirrors guide photons on their optical paths.

- **Optical Fibers**: Photons often travel through these fibers, which act like the dedicated tracks for our light-speed trains. The fibers ensure that photons reach their destination without external interference.

- **Photon Detectors**: At the end of a quantum computation or operation, we need to "read" the state of our photonic qubits. Specialized photon detectors capture the photons and convert their information into data we can interpret.

Working with photonic quantum systems is a dance of light and matter. Every beam splitter, mirror angle, and laser pulse is meticulously calibrated to ensure the quantum computations are executed flawlessly.

Building a quantum computer is more than just assembling these components; it's creating a harmonious, interconnected system. Like the best highway systems in the world, it's designed for efficiency, speed, and accuracy.

## Spin

*The Quantum Compass of Particles*

In the macroscopic world, when we think of 'spin', we might imagine a top rotating on a surface or Earth rotating around its axis. However, in quantum physics, 'spin' doesn't quite represent a literal spinning motion. Instead, it's an intrinsic property of particles, much like a fingerprint unique to each individual.

To visualize this, suppose spin is a tiny magnetic compass embedded within particles, specifically electrons, protons, and neutrons. Just as a compass needle points north due to Earth's magnetic field, quantum particles possess an innate orientation because of their spin. This orientation influences how these particles behave in the presence of external magnetic fields.

In a laboratory setting, physicists use high-powered magnets to probe the spins of particles. When subjected to an external magnetic field, a particle's spin will either align with the field, referred to as spin-up, or opposite to the field, known as spin-down. These two distinct orientations lead to different energy states for the particle, and this distinction is vital. It becomes one of the foundational stones upon which quantum computers are built.

Researchers can detect and manipulate these spins with the right tools, such as magnetic resonance machines. By adjusting the strength and orientation of the external magnetic fields, they can persuade particles to change their spin states. This ability to read and modify spin provides a robust platform for encoding and processing quantum information.

Spin is not just an abstract quantum number but a real, physical property. When harnessed correctly, it can be the very core of a quantum computer's memory and processing unit. Lab infrastructure, including advanced magnets and resonance machines, physically interacts with and manipulates these spins, bringing the mysterious quantum world to our fingertips.

# NMR

*The Quantum Maestro of Spin*

Nuclear Magnetic Resonance, or NMR for short, is a sophisticated technique. Imagine a maestro directing an orchestra of quantum spins. It's a method that allows scientists to probe and manipulate atomic nuclei's spin states, uncovering their secrets.

Picture attending a grand symphony, where the instruments are the atomic nuclei. Each instrument (nucleus) has its unique tone (spin). The maestro (NMR) ensures that every instrument plays in harmony, creating a coordinated melody rather than a cacophonous noise.

In practical terms, NMR places a sample inside a powerful magnetic field. This makes the nuclei in the sample resonate at specific frequencies. Then, by applying radiofrequency pulses, scientists can manipulate these resonances, effectively "playing" the nuclei like musical notes.

The equipment at the heart of an NMR-based quantum computer is the NMR spectrometer. This device is a culmination of multiple components:

1. **Magnet:** Often superconducting, this magnet creates a strong, uniform magnetic field where the sample is placed. The stronger the magnetic field, the more precise the resonance frequencies of the nuclei, much like tuning a musical instrument for optimal sound.

2.   **Probe:** This is where the sample resides. When exposed to radiofrequency pulses, the probe detects the nuclei's tiny magnetic responses.

3.   **Radiofrequency (RF) Transmitter:** This transmits short bursts or pulses of radio waves into the sample, causing specific nuclei to resonate.

4.   **Receiver:** After the RF pulse, nuclei return to their original states and emit signals. The receiver picks up these signals to extract information about the sample's nuclear environment.

In a quantum computing context, the spin states of the nuclei (either aligned with or against the magnetic field) can be interpreted as qubits. Scientists can use RF pulses to put these nuclei into superpositions of states or even entangle multiple nuclei, leveraging the principles of quantum mechanics for computation.

Thus, NMR is not just a bridge between the quantum and classical worlds; it's a physical interface. Quantum spins are read, written, and manipulated through instruments like the NMR spectrometer.

## Spin's Dance

*Superposition and Entanglement*

The mysterious quantum properties of superposition and entanglement are not just abstract ideas; they are the behavior of particles with spin. Let's revisit these properties using spin as our guide.

## 1. Superposition and Spin

In the context of the NMR techniques mentioned earlier, superposition is a cornerstone. When a nucleus is subjected to a radiofrequency pulse from the NMR spectrometer, it's nudged into a superposition of spin states. The nuclei aren't just aligned with or against the magnetic field; they exist in a delicate balance of both states. This phenomenon allows for the quantum parallelism that powers quantum computing's incredible potential.

## 2. Entanglement and Spin:

In our NMR-based quantum computer, entanglement is not just a fancy word; it's a physical operation. By carefully crafting sequences of radiofrequency pulses, scientists can make the spins of two nuclei become entangled. When this happens, the state of one nucleus becomes dependent on the state of the other, even if they're spatially separated. This allows for incredibly intricate and powerful quantum operations, as the state of one qubit (spin) can determine the state of another.

To capture the outcome of these quantum dances, scientists employ *quantum detectors* that can pick up the delicate signals of these phenomena. These detectors are sensitive to the slightest of changes and can confirm if spins are in superposition or entangled.

In essence, both are vital for encoding and processing quantum information. With tools like the NMR spectrometer, we aren't just reading about quantum principles; we're actively wielding them, using actual hardware to write and manipulate the very language of the quantum world.

## Concrete Examples of Spin

Spin, one of the intrinsic quantum properties of subatomic particles, isn't just a theoretical construct—it plays a vital role in countless quantum computing applications. These are realized physically, harnessing the very essence of quantum mechanics in the lab.

1. **Quantum Memory Devices:** In quantum computers, the state of a qubit, often represented by the spin of an electron or nucleus, can store information. This is similar to classical computer memory but with the quantum twist of superposition, allowing for more complex data storage. Storing quantum information using spin often requires ultra-cold environments. This is achieved using dilution refrigerators, which can chill devices to temperatures colder than outer space. Within these environments, magnetic fields or focused lasers might be used to manipulate the spin states of individual electrons or nuclei, allowing them to act as memory banks.

2. **Spin-based Quantum Logic Gates:** Classical computers utilize logic gates (AND, OR, NOT) to perform operations on bits, and quantum computers employ spin-based gates to manipulate qubits. For example, a specific electron spin can be flipped using carefully calibrated magnetic fields to match a quantum NOT gate operation. Physically controlling electron spins requires precision tools. Superconducting magnets, for instance, can generate the precise magnetic fields needed to control spins. Sometimes, precision microwave pulses are used to flip spins in a controlled

manner, acting as the physical implementation of certain quantum gates.

3. **Quantum Cryptography:** Quantum Key Distribution (QKD) is a process used in quantum cryptography. It leverages the entanglement property of particles. Spin is a vital component in this, where entangled photons' spins are measured to create cryptographic keys that are virtually unhackable. Implementing QKD involves sending and receiving entangled photons. To generate these, non-linear crystals are used, which can produce pairs of entangled photons when excited by a laser. On the receiving end, photon detectors, often made of superconducting materials, measure the photons' spins to extract the encryption key.

4. **Quantum Sensors:** Spin is used in quantum sensing applications to detect minute changes in physical quantities, like magnetic fields. By sensing the tiny shifts in spin states, these sensors can detect changes at unprecedented sensitivity levels. SQUIDs (Superconducting Quantum Interference Devices) are often used to detect discrete changes in spin states. These are highly sensitive magnetometers designed to measure extremely subtle magnetic fields, allowing us to identify tiny shifts in spin states.

5. **Spintronics:** These aren't quantum computers in the classical sense, but they leverage quantum properties for tasks like data storage and transfer. Here, spin is manipulated using electrical currents or optical methods to achieve desired outcomes. Spintronic devices often employ semiconductor materials, similar to what's used in today's computer chips, but with a twist: these materials have been engineered to be sensitive to electron spin. Ferromagnetic

electrodes can inject or detect spins in a controlled manner, and polarized light can be used to manipulate and read spin states.

These applications, built upon intricate setups and cutting-edge tools, are a testament to how the metaphysical concept of 'spin' is finding concrete, transformative use in the real world. Combining these advanced tools and techniques, quantum researchers and engineers can harness the power of spin and bring the quantum world a step closer to our daily lives.

## Quantum Computing Architectures

Venturing into the blueprints of quantum computing, we are greeted with various architectural designs, each displaying a unique approach to benefit from the quantum world's extraordinary powers. Just as architects design different types of buildings— skyscrapers, bungalows, or cottages—based on the purpose, terrain, and materials available, quantum scientists and engineers have crafted distinct computing models to optimize performance and address specific computational challenges. These architectural frameworks are not just conceptual; they have distinct hardware setups, specialized tools, and particular methodologies. Let's explore the architecture and elements that shape the backbone of quantum computers.

### Circuit Model

In the vast landscape of quantum computing architectures, the Circuit Model can be compared to the traditional blueprints used in constructing buildings. It represents a foundational approach where operations are structured in a sequence, much like the logical flow of electrical circuits in classical computing.

Physically, the Circuit Model is characterized by a network of quantum gates that act upon qubits. Each gate performs a specific operation on the qubits; when combined, they form a quantum circuit. To realize these circuits requires precise control of the qubits, typically achieved using techniques like laser pulses, microwave bursts, or specific magnetic interactions, depending on the type of qubit used.

In the lab, our Circuit Model applies to various devices. For instance, if superconducting qubits are employed, a dilution refrigerator, oscillators, and pulse generators are required to orchestrate the timing and nature of interactions between qubits. Additionally, high-precision measurement equipment will monitor and evaluate the outcomes.

The Circuit Model represents a systematic, step-by-step approach. Each operation is like laying one brick atop another in building construction, with every element carefully placed to ensure the stability and functionality of the final structure.

*Measurement-Based Model*

The Measurement-Based Model, sometimes called the "one-way quantum computer," introduces a unique twist to the world of quantum computing architectures. Suppose the Circuit Model is a carefully designed blueprint. In that case, the Measurement-Based Model is like constructing a building with many prefabricated rooms, deciding its final shape and function by how these rooms are interconnected and accessed.

Creating this model involves preparing a large, highly entangled quantum state known as a "cluster state." Think of this as a vast interconnected web of qubits, each holding potential pathways for quantum computation. The true magic begins when specific measurements are made on these qubits. By measuring individual qubits in a particular sequence and manner, the rest of the qubits adjust and evolve their states accordingly.

In the lab, the Measurement-Based Model demands high-fidelity audio preparation of the initial cluster state and precise measurement tools. Photonic systems are often favored for this approach due to the ease with which photons can be entangled and measured. Here, beam splitters, which divide light paths, become integral, as do single-photon detectors, which identify and quantify the properties of individual light particles. These detectors, often cooled to reduce noise, provide the feedback necessary to guide the subsequent measurements and quantum operations.

In many ways, the Measurement-Based Model is like a dynamic puzzle. While you start with a vast, interconnected potential of quantum information, the final computational outcome is sculpted by the decisions made during the measurement process, each choice refining and guiding the quantum computation to its conclusion.

*Adiabatic Model*

The Adiabatic Model offers a different concept of evolution and gradual change. If we bring our architectural analogy back, consider the Adiabatic Model akin to constructing a bridge by starting on one side of a depth and slowly extending it until it reaches the other side. Instead of explicitly programming each step, the structure simply evolves in response to the landscape.

In the quantum domain, this model begins with a quantum system in a well-understood initial state. The system is then subjected to a slowly changing external influence, ensuring that the system remains in its lowest energy state, or "ground state", throughout the process. The end goal? To evolve the system into a final state that represents the solution to a given computational problem.

Realizing the Adiabatic Model in a physical setup involves a meticulously designed quantum system where interactions and external influences can be finely tuned. The equipment and tools needed to achieve this are quite specialized:

1. **Magnetic Fields & Superconducting Loops**: The behavior of qubits in this model is often governed by magnetic fields, where superconducting loops can serve as qubits. Tiny changes in these magnetic fields guide the evolution of the system.

2. **Control Units**: These devices ensure that external influences change slowly and predictably. They are precision-engineered to deliver accurate and gradual shifts, ensuring the quantum system remains in its ground state.

3. **Cryogenic Systems**: The adiabatic process often requires extremely low temperatures to minimize external noise and ensure accuracy. Thus, cryogenic cooling systems become indispensable to maintaining these chilly conditions.

4. **Advanced Monitoring Equipment**: Given the gradual evolution in the Adiabatic Model, real-time monitoring of the system's state is crucial. This is done using sophisticated sensors and detectors to gauge even the slightest changes in the quantum state.

The Adiabatic Model banks on the principle of slow and steady evolution, rather than discrete steps. It allows the quantum system to find its path, navigating the intricate quantum landscape and eventually revealing the solution to the computational challenge at hand.

Beyond the primary architectures we've explored, it's worth noting that other computational models leverage quantum mechanics. For instance, the **Quantum Cellular Automata** operate by local interactions on a lattice, while the **Topological Quantum Computing Model** exploits the intricate world of quantum braids in specific materials. Though these may sound mysterious now, they're part of the broader landscape of computational innovations that scientists and researchers intensely explore.

Quantum computing isn't a static field; it's vibrant and ever-evolving. Researchers worldwide push the boundaries daily, exploring new architectures, models, and paradigms. Their work, often hidden in lab journals and complex research papers, is like the tireless endeavors of gold miners—chipping away steadily in the hope of unearthing a groundbreaking method or principle. This dynamic nature is what makes quantum computing so exciting. The architectures we've covered are just the tip of the iceberg, and there's a thrilling sense of anticipation in the quantum community about what might be the next big discovery!

These architectures—whether circuit-based, measurement-driven, or adiabatic—are more than just theoretical constructs; they're the foundational pillars on which quantum systems are built. Each offers a unique perspective on how to harness the elusive powers of quantum mechanics. And while these models provide a roadmap, the journey—the experiments, the challenges, the breakthroughs— truly define the quantum revolution.

## Different Approaches in Quantum Computing

As we transition from the thirty-thousand-foot view of quantum computing, it becomes pivotal to understand the platforms up close where these ideas take shape. These platforms represent the machinery, the hardware that hums from the activity in labs around the world. Here, we'll visit three of the most promising and widely studied approaches: superconducting circuits, trapped ions, and topological qubits.

## Superconducting Circuits

*Where Currents Race Unhindered*

Imagine a microscopic racetrack where electrical currents dash about, uninhibited by resistance. This isn't some sci-fi concept but the intricate domain of superconducting circuits. Crafted from unique materials that, when cooled to temperatures barely above absolute zero, offer no resistance to electrical flow. Such conditions form the backdrop for the quantum computation marvel within these circuits.

**Principle**: At the heart of these circuits lie the quantum properties of superconducting materials. The electric current flows unopposed in this chilly quantum freezer, forming the container for our qubit operations. A vital actor on this microscopic stage is the 'Josephson junction'. Imagine it as a gatekeeper allowing current to flow between superconductors, playing an essential role in computation.

*In the Lab*

Step into a lab dedicated to superconducting circuits, and you'd likely first be drawn to an imposing structure resembling a large metallic chandelier. A 'dilution refrigerator'. Its purpose? To plunge the environment housing our superconducting qubits to temperatures colder than the vast expanses of outer space, ensuring they remain in their unique superconducting state. Surrounding this behemoth are arrays of machines that generate precise microwave pulses. These pulses manipulate our qubits, giving them a computational task. After each operation, advanced measurement devices await, ready to interpret and reveal the quantum states of the qubits once their tasks are complete.

Engaging with these quantum computers is like conducting a symphony. With a blend of calculated anticipation and rehearsed skill, scientists send a series of commands, instructing machines to generate exact microwave sequences. This intricate dance of commands and responses between humans and machines is what gives birth to quantum computations.

*Hardware and Materials*

Superconducting qubits are a marvel of modern engineering. They're fabricated from thin layers of superconducting materials on a silicon or sapphire substrate. The most commonly used materials include aluminum for the superconducting layer and silicon or sapphire for the substrate. Key to the operation of these qubits is the Josephson junction, a non-superconducting barrier (often insulating or semiconducting) sandwiched between superconducting layers.

*Tools and Equipment*

The precision required in fabricating superconducting qubits is staggering. Labs utilize electron beam lithography to intricately design the quantum circuits at a nanoscale level. Furthermore, dilution refrigerators, which resemble large metallic chandeliers, plunge the qubits to near absolute zero temperatures, providing an almost noise-free environment essential for quantum operations. Microwave pulse generators are employed to manipulate the state of the qubits; each pulse is carefully calibrated for optimal qubit interaction.

*Software and Interaction*

Precision in quantum computation is paramount, so tailored software interfaces are deployed. These software platforms allow scientists to design quantum algorithms, feed them to the hardware, and interpret the outcomes. Often, a classical computer runs this software, acting as a bridge between human inputs and quantum processes.

*Properties*

Superconducting qubits are artificial atoms made from circuits of capacitors and Josephson junctions. They operate based on the quantum principles of superposition and entanglement, using the flow of electrical current as their mode of operation.

*Stability*

These qubits offer strong stability owing to their macroscopic nature. However, they're sensitive to external electromagnetic noise, which can introduce errors.

*Coherence Times*

Currently, in 2024, coherence times for superconducting qubits have reached tens to hundreds of microseconds. While this might seem short, it's impressive in the quantum world and allows for a reasonable number of quantum operations to be performed sequentially.

*Scalability*

Superconducting qubits have a strong case for scalability. With companies like Google and IBM investing heavily in this technology, we've seen rapid advancements in multi-qubit systems. Cross-talk between qubits remains a challenge, but innovations in chip design and error-correction protocols pave the way for larger, more powerful superconducting quantum computers.

# Trapped Ions

*Dancing Particles in an Electro-Magnetic Ballet*

Visualize, for a moment, a shimmering dance floor suspended in space, where ions – charged atomic particles – pirouette and glide in a choreographed performance. This is no celestial ballroom but the captivating arena of trapped ion quantum computing.

## Principle

The foundational idea here revolves around using individual ions as qubits. These ions are "trapped" or suspended in space using electromagnetic fields. Their very state of being, whether they spin one way or another, is what encodes our quantum information. By using lasers, scientists can excite or change the state of these ions, making them suitable for quantum computation.

## In the Lab

Enter the lab, and you'll likely be captivated by a piece of equipment that seems plucked from the minds of science fiction: the ion trap. This device, often made of gold or other metals and resembling a micro, intricately designed crown, holds our dancing ions in place. Hovering above, specialized lasers target each ion with pinpoint precision. These lasers, often mounted on adjustable arms or platforms, are the conductors of our quantum dance, coaxing ions into their computational twirls with flashes of controlled light.

Interaction with this system requires a skillful touch. Scientists, adorned in lab coats, carefully calibrate these lasers, ensuring they emit the perfect frequency and intensity of light. As the lasers interact with the ions, they induce quantum jumps, changing their spins and allowing the computation to occur. Once this dance is done, specialized detectors stand ready, analyzing the afterglow of the ions to decode the results.

In this harmonious union of charged particles, electromagnetic fields, and precise lasers, the trapped ion approach promises computations of incredible delicacy and precision, all choreographed to the tune of quantum mechanics.

### Hardware and Materials

At the core of trapped ion quantum computers are individual ions suspended in free space using electromagnetic fields. The beauty of this approach is in its natural atomic structure, where electrons orbiting the nucleus exhibit quantum properties ideal for computation. The choice of ion varies, but ions of Ytterbium, Calcium, and Barium have been favored.

### Tools and Equipment

To hold these ions in place, a series of electrodes generate the necessary electromagnetic fields, creating what's known as a Paul trap. Once trapped, finely tuned lasers target individual ions, manipulating their quantum states. Photodetectors and cameras then capture emitted photons from these ions to show their quantum state.

### Software and Interaction

Custom software interfaces help choreograph laser pulses, ensuring that ions are manipulated in a sequence corresponding to the desired quantum algorithm. Real-time feedback loops may be implemented to adjust laser parameters dynamically, ensuring high-fidelity operations.

*Properties*

These qubits are based on individual ions trapped in electromagnetic fields. The quantum state is often stored in the electron configuration around the ion's nucleus.

*Stability*

Ions are naturally occurring entities with inherently stable quantum states. The very act of trapping them provides an isolated environment, reducing external disruptions.

*Coherence Times*

Trapped ions boast some of the longest coherence times among physical qubits, often reaching many seconds, depending on the ion type and trap environment.

*Scalability*

While individual trapped ions are high-quality qubits, scaling up remains challenging. This is due to the increased complexity of controlling large numbers of ions simultaneously and the logistical challenges of managing more extensive trapping arrays.

## Topological Qubits

Imagine a city's roadway, not as a simple flat grid but as a series of intertwined and knotted overpasses and underpasses, where the structure of the road itself holds significance. In this intricate web, the overall framework remains undisturbed, even if there's a minor disruption in one part. Just as these knots or braids in the road protect against simple obstructions, topological qubits use the "knots" of quantum states to guard against errors.

*Principle*

The essence of topological quantum computing is in its very name - "topology," the study of properties of space that are preserved under continuous transformations. These braided paths in a two-dimensional space determine the states of topological qubits. Due to their knotted nature, they're highly resistant to local errors, a constant challenge in quantum computing. The information is stored not in a specific place but in the twists and turns of these quantum braids.

*In the Lab*

A laboratory focused on topological quantum computing would have an array of highly specialized equipment designed to manipulate and study two-dimensional materials like quantum wells. These setups help generate and study quasi-particles called anyons, which have fractional quantum numbers and are at the heart of topological quantum computations. Cryogenic equipment, similar to the superconducting setup but specialized for these materials, ensures the system remains at ultra-cold temperatures. Microscopes with incredibly high resolution, such as scanning tunneling microscopes, are employed to observe and manipulate the quantum braids directly, allowing scientists to "weave" the quantum knots.

In a "quiet" and ultra-controlled lab environment, scientists coax certain materials into a two-dimensional existence, where particles behave unlike anything in our everyday world. With their fractional charge and unique braiding behavior, the anyons become the heroes of this quantum story. The topological qubit's resilience stems from its spatial properties — it's like trying to erase a knot from a twisted rubber band without actually untwisting it. The data isn't in one loop or twist but in the overall braid. This resilience promises more stable and error-resistant computations, with scientists delicately guiding and observing these braids in action while nestled in the embrace of advanced cryogenic chambers.

*Hardware and Materials*

Topological qubits are a newcomer in the quantum arena. They use certain quasi-particles, called anyons, that exist in specific two-dimensional materials. The magic here is in the braiding of these anyons—by moving them around one another, quantum information is stored in a manner that's reliable against local disturbances.

*Tools and Equipment*

To realize topological qubits, labs require ultra-pure material samples where these anyons can emerge. Advanced microscopy techniques, like scanning tunneling microscopy, help visualize and manipulate anyons' braids at the subatomic scale.

### Software and Interaction

Software tools are still emerging in the developing stage of topological quantum computing. These tools help in the design and simulation of anyon braiding operations. Additionally, they allow error-checking, given that topological qubits promise better resistance to quantum errors.

### Stability

The topological nature makes these qubits highly stable. Local errors, which plague other qubit types, do not easily disrupt topological qubits.

### Coherence Times

Though still in the early stages of research, early findings suggest that topological qubits can have extended coherence times, potentially even surpassing trapped ions, though this remains to be definitively established.

### Scalability

The principle behind topological qubits suggests excellent scalability due to their inherent error resistance. However, practical implementation is still in its infancy, with scalability largely untested in real-world setups.

## Comparing the Quantum Titans

*Superconducting Circuits, Trapped Ions, and Topological Qubits*

The three dominant quantum technologies showcase the blend of advanced materials, intricate tools, and state-of-the-art software that facilitates quantum computation. Each approach is rooted in the same quantum principles but leverages unique physical properties and requires specialized tools and techniques for realization. The field is expansive, and as we'll see, each system comes with its set of advantages and challenges.

While superconducting qubits ride the wave of industrial investment and scaling up, trapped ions offer remarkable integrity and stability. Meanwhile, topological qubits present a promising but largely uncharted territory, potentially unlocking the next era of quantum computation. The quantum race is very much alive, with each technology vying for dominance in a rapidly evolving landscape.

Navigating the quantum highway, one can't help but marvel at the architectural wonders: the superconducting superhighways, the mesmerizing dance of trapped ions, and the intricately knotted lanes of topological qubits. But as with any engineering marvel, each has its strengths and its Achilles' heel.

## Superconducting Circuits

*Strengths*

Quick, efficient, and capable of maintaining quantum states for an extended period. Their relative maturity means we've got a head start with them.

*Limitations*

Extremely sensitive to their environment; the slightest external interference can disrupt their operations.

*Best Suited For*

General-purpose quantum computations, especially with the current muscle of research and major industry backing.

## Trapped Ions

*Strengths*

High precision and very long coherence times make them fantastic for operations requiring extended computations.

*Limitations*

Scaling up – adding more ions to the system – is a notable challenge due to cluttered interactions.

*Best Suited For*

Specialized quantum tasks that benefit from high precision and long coherence but don't need a vast number of qubits.

## Topological Qubits

*Strengths*

Their braided nature offers unmatched resilience to local errors, potentially simplifying error correction.

*Limitations*

Still in the research phase, creating and manipulating anyons in a controlled environment remains challenging.

*Best Suited For*

Quantum computations that require high stability and low error rates once they progress beyond the research phase.

## A Glimpse Beyond the Horizon

The domain of quantum computing, ever mysterious and intriguing, never ceases to surprise us. While these three titans dominate our current landscape, the quantum frontier is vast and uncharted. Tomorrow, we might discover new pathways, perhaps even harnessing the power of quantum computers to pave the way for their successors. Imagine a world where quantum systems, birthed from the very phenomena they seek to harness, guide us toward the next leap in computational evolution. As we continue this quantum journey, the future is abundant, promising innovations beyond our wildest dreams.

# Creating Scalable Quantum Networks

As quantum systems scale up, they consistently encounter more opportunities for errors. Even tiny disturbances – a stray photon, slight temperature fluctuations, or electromagnetic noise – can disrupt a qubit's state. In classical computers, errors are managed with redundancy, for instance, by using multiple transistors to represent a single bit. Quantum systems require a more detailed approach, leading to the development of fault-tolerant quantum computing.

# Fault-tolerant Quantum Computing

*Principle*

The idea here is not to prevent quantum errors but to detect and correct them without measuring, thereby destroying the quantum state. This is achieved using specially designed quantum error-correcting codes, which can recognize when qubits go astray and guide them back without collapsing their delicate superpositions.

*Hardware and Tools*

To implement fault tolerance, a quantum computer needs additional qubits — called ancilla qubits — to monitor the primary qubits responsible for the computation. Specialized gates are used to entangle the ancilla qubits with the computational ones, allowing errors to be detected and corrected. This introduces more hardware complexity, demanding many more qubits for each logical, error-corrected qubit.

## Scalable Quantum Networks

*Principle*

A scalable quantum network aims to link multiple quantum devices into a unified, interconnected system, similar to today's internet but operating on quantum principles.

*Hardware and Tools*

Establishing such networks requires the creation of quantum repeaters (devices that can receive, amplify, and re-transmit quantum signals without destroying their quantum nature) and the ability to convert quantum signals to different forms suitable for long-distance transmission, typically using photons.

## NV Center-in-Diamond

An emerging and intriguing quantum computing and networking approach hinges on a naturally occurring diamond defect.

*Principle*

At the heart of this technology is the Nitrogen-Vacancy (NV) center — a spot where a nitrogen atom replaces a carbon atom next to a vacant site in the diamond lattice. This defect has an electron spin that can be manipulated and measured using light, making it a candidate for a qubit.

*Hardware and Tools*

Diamond chips housing NV centers are the primary substrates for this technology. Green lasers are typically used to manipulate the

NV center's spin state. Microwaves can then control the spin, and red light is emitted from the NV center when it returns to its ground state, providing a means to read out its quantum state. The entire setup, while compact, requires precision optics, stabilized laser systems, and advanced photon detectors.

By harnessing the NV center's sensitivity to electromagnetic fields, it's also been proposed as a quantum sensor, with applications in fields as varied as biology (imaging cellular processes) and geology (detecting mineral deposits).

Tapping into fault tolerance is pivotal for quantum computers to realize their revolutionary potential. By ensuring errors are kept in check and by linking quantum systems together in scalable networks, we inch closer to a quantum internet. Technologies like the NV Center-in-Diamond further expand the horizon, reminding us that the quantum space is rich with potential waiting to be tapped.

## Quantum Computing with Neutral Atoms

At the frontier of quantum research, neutral atoms stand out as a promising medium for quantum computation. Unlike charged ions or electrons that experience strong coulombic interactions (attraction or force between electric charges), neutral atoms interact weakly, offering a distinctive set of advantages and challenges.

*Principle*

Neutral atoms, especially alkali atoms like rubidium, have distinct energy levels that can be harnessed as qubit states. Their interactions, governed by quantum mechanics, can be exploited to perform quantum gates.

*Hardware and Tools*

Precision tools are paramount to manipulating these neutral atoms and bring out their computing potential.

1.   **Optical Traps:** These are essentially "tweezers" of light. Lasers are meticulously tuned such that their intensity creates tiny traps that can hold and manipulate individual atoms in space. Picture a landscape of dimples or pockets where each atom rests, all made and controlled using laser beams.

2.   **Magnetic Fields:** These are applied to tweak the atomic states, allowing for subtle control over the qubits.

3.   **Laser Beams for Quantum Gates:** Specific laser pulses can make neutral atoms interact in a controlled way, enacting quantum gates that are fundamental for computation.

4.   **High-resolution Imaging Systems:** These capture the light from the atoms, allowing scientists to read out the quantum information after a computation.

The whole arrangement might remind you of a high-tech light show, with ultra-cold neutral atoms dancing and interacting under the spell of lasers in a carefully choreographed performance.

# Optical Traps

These devices represent a triumph of marrying quantum mechanics with photonics.

*Principle*

At the heart of optical trapping is the concept that light can exert a force on matter. When an atom or small particle encounters a focused laser beam, its photons can push or pull on that particle, effectively "trapping" it in a specific location.

*Hardware and Tools*

1. **Tunable Lasers:** These are the backbone of optical traps. By adjusting the laser's intensity and focus, researchers can create pockets of varying depths and sizes suitable for holding everything from individual atoms to small biological molecules.

2. **Microscopic Objectives:** Just as they sound, these microscope components focus the laser beams down to the required minuscule sizes.

3. **Feedback Mechanisms:** These systems quickly adjust the laser's properties in real-time to maintain the trap, especially when dealing with dynamic systems or particles that might try to escape.

The visualization here is like a futuristic game of marbles, where each marble (atom or particle) is held still, not by a hand or container, but by beams of light. In labs, you'd find scientists peering into advanced optical systems, adjusting lasers, and observing the behavior of trapped particles with fascination.

Both neutral atom quantum computing and optical trapping highlight the ingenious ways scientists manipulate the microscopic world. Each flicker of light in these setups isn't just illumination; it's a tool, a hand, a gate, or a bridge in the quantum domain. The magic is in the quantum properties being harnessed and the innovative tools built to do so.

## The Technical Challenges and Advancements associated with each Technology

## 1. Superconducting Qubits

*Challenges*

- **Decoherence:** Though superconducting qubits have relatively long coherence times, they are still prone to errors due to their interactions with the environment.

- **Manufacturing Precision:** Creating high-quality Josephson junctions and other components at the nanoscale requires meticulous precision.

- **Temperature Requirements:** Operating near absolute zero presents technical and energy cost challenges.

*Advancements*

- **Improved Materials:** Research has led to the development of superconducting materials that offer better performance and resilience.

- **Error Correction Codes:** Techniques to identify and rectify quantum errors are maturing, enhancing the reliability of computations.

## 2. Trapped Ions

*Challenges*

- **Scalability:** Integrating large numbers of trapped ions while maintaining precise control over each is a daunting task.

- **Interference:** External electromagnetic interference can adversely affect the qubits, leading to computational errors.

*Advancements*

- **Modular Architectures:** Instead of one large trap, researchers are exploring interconnected modules, each holding a few ions.

- **Improved Lasers:** Technological enhancements in lasers allow for more precise manipulations and interactions between ions.

## 3. Topological Qubits

*Challenges*

- **Uncharted Territory:** Topological qubits are relatively new, making the experimental verification and scaling up more complex.

- **Error Rates:** While theoretically less prone to errors, practical implementations of topological qubits still face challenges in maintaining low error rates.

*Advancements*

- **Research on Majorana Fermions:** Breakthroughs in understanding these exotic particles pave the way for more reliable topological quantum computing.

- **Material Science:** Discoveries of new materials that can host these fermions have been critical.

## 4. Neutral Atoms and Optical Traps

*Challenges*

- **Control:** Manipulating a large array of neutral atoms with consistency is tricky.

- **Integration:** Integrating optical traps into scalable quantum systems without compromising performance is challenging.

- Advancements

- **Improved Imaging Techniques:** Advancements in imaging allow for better observation and manipulation of atoms within traps.

- **Dynamic Trap Configurations:** Researchers can now dynamically reconfigure optical traps, granting them more flexibility in quantum operations.

Every quantum technology, while holding immense potential, is a double-edged sword. The very properties that make them suitable for quantum computation also present challenges. Yet, the relentless march of research and innovation is steadily turning these challenges into stepping stones, pushing the frontier of what's possible in the quantum field.

## Evaluating Economic Factors, Power Capabilities, and Prevalence

Above, we've examined the microcosmic highways of qubits and the very architectures that define quantum computing. Yet, like any marvel of modern engineering, the quantum computer is not just a product of scientific curiosity; it's standing at the crossroads of feasibility, economics, and environmental considerations. As Leonard Susskind and Art Friedman might discuss over a cup of coffee, the grand theories and intricate mechanics of quantum computing must eventually meet our world's practical and economic realities.

This section will venture beyond the quantum gates and algorithms, stepping into the broader landscape where quantum computing intersects with economics, power dynamics, and global adoption trends. We'll weigh the costs against the computational wonders, ponder the power needs of these incredible machines, and gauge where we currently stand in the global race toward quantum supremacy.

*Practicality of Quantum Methods*

In our bid to understand the scope of quantum computing, it's tempting to focus solely on its scientific marvels. However, like any transformative technology, its ascent to mainstream application depends heavily on economic viability. Imagine the grand scientific conferences one might attend, similar to the boardroom meetings where CFOs and CEOs debate the cost and potential returns of venturing into quantum computing.

- **Capital Investment**: The initial investment required is at the heart of the economic discourse. Building a quantum computer isn't just about having a lab filled with scientists; it's about collecting the right materials, using specialized equipment like dilution refrigerators or laser systems, and maintaining an environment conducive to quantum phenomena. This isn't your typical startup cost but an endeavor that requires significant capital.

- **Operational Costs**: Once a quantum computer is up and running, the expenses don't stop. The immense cooling needs of superconducting qubits, the precision control systems for trapped ions, and the robust error-correction mechanisms for topological qubits—all add to the operational overhead. Additionally, there's the often-overlooked cost of training personnel to operate and maintain these machines.

- **Economies of Scale**: Just as the cost of producing a single unit of a new technology tends to drop as production scales up, the quantum industry will likely experience economies of scale. However, it's worth noting that we're still in the early phases, and scaling quantum technology will present its unique set of challenges and opportunities.

- **Monetizing Quantum Power**: The true economic potential of quantum computers lies in their applications. Financial modeling, drug discovery, and optimization problems are just a few domains where quantum computers can outshine their classical counterparts. But how quickly industries adopt and are willing to pay for quantum solutions remains a crucial economic question.

- **Long-term Implications**: Quantum computing isn't a flash in the pan; it's a long-term investment. While the initial costs are high, the potential for breakthroughs in various fields could lead to unprecedented returns. Moreover, the nations and corporations leading the quantum race today might find themselves holding significant geopolitical or market advantages in the future.

It's a conundrum similar to the early days of the silicon revolution. The initial chips were expensive, had limited applications, and were housed in room-sized computers. Yet, visionaries saw beyond these limitations, envisioning a world transformed by silicon. Today's quantum pioneers face steep challenges, but they're driven by a vision of a world where the rules of quantum mechanics don't just exist in textbooks but actively shape industries and economies.

*Adoption of Quantum Technologies*

Discussing the world of quantum often evokes imagery of vast, cutting-edge tech labs nestled within Silicon Valley. However, the fabric of quantum computing adoption weaves far beyond the empires of tech giants. The practical application and hardware infrastructure of quantum computing is an expanding field attracting diverse industries and research institutions alike.

1.    **Tech Powerhouses**: As expected, the usual suspects—Google, IBM, Intel, and Microsoft—are at the forefront of quantum research and have already developed their quantum processors. Their interests aren't merely academic; they envision quantum computers bolstering their core services, from cloud computing to artificial intelligence.

2.    **Academia and Research Institutions**: Universities across the globe, from MIT to the University of Queensland, are diving deep into the quantum realm. These institutions contribute significantly to the theoretical underpinnings and actively craft prototypes, often collaborating with industry leaders.

3.    **Aerospace and Defense**: The strategic advantages of quantum computing are alluring to defense contractors and aerospace industries. The potential for cracking cryptographic codes, optimizing complex logistical operations, and simulating intricate systems has led companies like Lockheed Martin and Airbus to invest heavily in quantum research and development.

4.   **Finance and Banking**: Surprisingly, the world of finance is also peeking into the quantum domain. Large banks and financial institutions are exploring quantum algorithms for portfolio optimization, risk analysis, and fraud detection. Their quantum pursuits might still be in the beginning stages, but they clearly recognize the transformative power.

5.   **Pharmaceuticals and Healthcare**: The complex dance of molecules and the daunting task of drug discovery might soon be revolutionized with quantum algorithms. Companies like Roche and Pfizer are starting to examine drug design and molecular simulations, hinting at a future where treatments are optimized at the quantum level.

6.   **Energy Sector**: The challenges of renewable energy storage, optimization of grid distribution, and exploration of new energy sources are areas where quantum computing might play a pivotal role. Energy giants like Shell and ExxonMobil are closely monitoring quantum advancements and beginning to funnel resources into research.

While the infrastructure required for quantum computing—like ultra-low temperature coolers and intricate lab equipment—might initially appear daunting and confined to specialized labs, there's a clear trend toward decentralization. As the technology matures and becomes more commercially viable, it's not too far-fetched to envision quantum processors humming away in the control rooms of various industries, from pharmaceuticals to finance. Quantum hardware, once the exclusive domain of specialized tech labs, is poised to permeate diverse sectors, reshaping how enterprises function.

## Solving Error Correction

*Noise, Errors, and Decoherence in Quantum Systems*

To grasp the quantum landscape fully, one must come to terms with its inherent unpredictability and fragility. Quantum systems, while potent, are like delicately tuned instruments; even the slightest interference can throw them off.

*Quantum Noise*

Picture a tranquil lake on a windless day. Every small pebble thrown into it creates ripples, disturbing its untouched stillness. In the quantum world, this "lake" is our carefully prepared quantum state, and the "pebbles" represent quantum noise – those unwanted, external agitations that can distort our computations. This noise can emanate from thermal vibrations, electromagnetic waves, or even cosmic rays.

*Quantum Errors*

These are the inevitable mistakes that arise during quantum operations. If you think of quantum computations like an intricate dance, a quantum error is a misstep. It can occur during the processing or the reading of quantum data. Sometimes, it's a bit flip (where a qubit changes from 0 to 1 or vice versa) or a phase flip (a shift in the qubit's phase). While individual errors can be minor, their collective impact can be detrimental, especially in large quantum circuits.

*Decoherence*

The real nemesis of any quantum computer. It's the process where quantum systems lose their quantum behavior and start acting classical. A good analogy might be the transition from a dream state (where anything is possible) to waking reality (where we are bound by the laws of classical physics). Decoherence is primarily caused by the quantum system's interactions with its environment. Every time a qubit interacts with the external world—be it a stray photon or molecule—it loses a bit of its quantumness.

Our still pond symbolizes our ideally stable qubit. When you drop a pebble in, the ripples that form represent the anticipated quantum state. But quantum systems are delicate. Raindrops, signifying quantum noise, can pepper the pond's surface. These droplets introduce unforeseen disturbances. Similar to the unpredictability of real-world factors like heat or electromagnetic interference. Each drop slightly shifts our qubit's state, obscuring its clarity.

Then, consider a sudden gust of wind as a direct quantum error. These gusts might be errors in how we control or read our qubits. They don't just disturb the water — they change the ripple pattern entirely. In this context, raindrops and wind gusts illuminate the diverse challenges and intrusions that quantum systems confront, underscoring the complexity of quantum computation.

Addressing these disturbances is paramount in the race to build scalable quantum computers. Not only do they challenge the integrity of quantum information, but they also remind us of the delicate balance between the quantum and classical worlds. The next step? Designing mechanisms to counteract these errors is where quantum error correction comes into play.

## Error Correction Techniques and Codes

A safety net becomes imperative in the intricate dance of quantum computation, where the tiniest disturbances can lead to catastrophic errors. Enter quantum error correction (QEC), our answer to the unpredictable quirks of the quantum domain. Much like classical error correction ensures the accuracy of bits in a classical computer, quantum error correction does so for qubits.

*1. Quantum Error Correction Codes (QECC)*

These codes are the language we've developed to combat quantum noise and errors. A primary example is the Shor code, designed by Peter Shor, which can correct random single-qubit errors. Instead of just using a single qubit to store a quantum bit of information, the Shor code uses nine qubits. This nine-qubit system can identify and correct any errors affecting its individual members, safeguarding the quantum information.

*2. The Surface Code*

Another fascinating technique, the surface code, takes advantage of a two-dimensional lattice of qubits. The unique layout allows errors to be spotted and rectified efficiently as they manifest along the lattice lines. This makes the surface code particularly robust and has been a favorite among researchers for its relatively higher error threshold.

### 3. Cat Codes

These are inspired by the famous Schrödinger's cat thought experiment. This setup uses superpositions of coherent states — states in which wave phases are the same —. When errors occur, they shift the phase. These shifts become detectable due to the unique properties of the superpositions, enabling timely corrections.

Imagine a masterful orchestra where each musician (qubit) must play in perfect harmony. Even if a few go off-tune (errors), these correction techniques act like a conductor, identifying the off-notes and guiding the musicians back to harmony. The result? Quantum symphonies that resonate with precision, even amidst the chaos.

Achieving reliable QEC, however, is no simple feat. It requires a multitude of qubits and sophisticated algorithms. But the progress in this arena has been promising, laying the foundation for larger, more reliable quantum machines soon.

## Challenges in Achieving High-Fidelity Qubit Operations

In quantum computing, achieving high-fidelity qubit operations is one of the most formidable challenges. Think of fidelity in this context as the trustworthiness of a qubit to execute its job accurately. Just as an expert pianist strives for each note to be pitch-perfect in a concert, we desire each qubit operation to be flawless in a computation. But, much like that pianist facing disturbances from a mistuned instrument or a noisy environment, our qubits have to deal with multiple issues.

## 1. External Environmental Disturbances

The outside world is full of activity—vibrations, temperature fluctuations, electromagnetic fields. These can sneak into the delicately protected quantum domain and cause disturbances. The fragility of quantum states, especially entanglements, makes them exceptionally susceptible to such external interferences.

## 2. Hardware Imperfections

Even the slightest material defects or impurities can influence qubit behavior. This is particularly relevant for superconducting qubits, where microscopic imperfections can lead to substantial irregularities. Also, the equipment used to manipulate and read out qubits—like microwave pulses in superconducting circuits—must operate with impeccable accuracy. A slight misalignment or malfunction can skew results.

## 3. Decoherence

As previously discussed, quantum systems tend to lose their unique quantum characteristics over time due to interactions with their environments—a phenomenon termed decoherence. The longer a qubit can maintain its quantum state before succumbing to decoherence, the better. However, ensuring long coherence times is challenging due to the inherent instability of quantum states.

## 4. Error Accumulation

Even minor error rates can accumulate in extended quantum computations, leading to significant problems. For quantum computers to be practically helpful, these error rates must be reduced to below certain thresholds, a challenge that requires hardware improvements and innovative error correction techniques.

## 5. Scaling Up

While we might achieve high-fidelity operations with a handful of qubits, scaling this to hundreds, thousands, or even millions of qubits without compromising accuracy is a herculean task. As the number of qubits increases, so does the potential for errors and the complexity of error correction.

How to manage a colossal orchestra with various instruments. The larger it grows, the harder it becomes to ensure each musician is in perfect sync, and the challenge intensifies when they're playing a piece that demands intricate coordination.

Despite these challenges, the field is advancing steadily. Each hurdle, while substantial, spurs innovation and refinement, pushing us closer to the era where quantum computers could redefine our technological landscape.

## Quantum Hardware & Ecosystem

*Problem-Solving Quantum Tech*

In the intricate dance of technology, quantum computing has gracefully transitioned from chalkboard theories to physical phenomena in cutting-edge labs. This section goes into the monumental strides of quantum hardware, painting a picture of an ecosystem on the cusp of reshaping computational boundaries.

Central to the evolution of quantum machinery is the marriage between quantum mechanics and materials science. Qubit stability—required for quantum processing and storage—builds its foundation from the very materials it's sculpted from. Princeton's groundbreaking study weaves this narrative, spotlighting how material advancements will be a pillar for quantum computers' future sophistication. Key takeaways include:

1.   The essence of quantum development is firmly anchored in materials science. Princeton's insights reveal how materials—from the precision of superconducting circuits to the subtlety of trapped ions—are pivotal in crafting trustworthy qubits, the heartbeats of quantum machines.

- Quantum computing's journey, while bursting with achievements, hasn't been without its set of problems. Quantum states' delicate nature demands innovative error correction and qubit stabilization. Furthermore, the quest for efficient quantum interconnects (QuIC) illuminates the importance of open communication in quantum architectures.

- A mass adoption in quantum algorithm design is unfolding, harnessing the inherent qualities of quantum mechanics, such as entanglement and superposition. These emerging algorithms beckon solutions for herculean tasks, from deciphering cryptographic enigmas to pioneering materials science research.

- From its embryonic stages, colored with academic curiosity, quantum computing has soared, attracting government and tech titans. Their collective vision? To unlock the game-changing capacities of quantum systems.

As quantum computing charts its path forward, the nuances of hardware and material sciences become its foundational pillars. The dance between qubit architectures and the materials that form them plays a primary role in defining the future. We will scan the quantum hardware landscape to see its challenges and breakthroughs. It is time to spotlight how material sciences support and actively shape this dynamic journey.

## Material Sciences

*Sculpting the Backbone of Quantum Computing*

In quantum computing, the substance lies not just in mathematical algorithms but deeply in the fabric from which these machines are woven: their materials. The meticulous engineering and crafting are the passage between quantum theories and real-world quantum computers.

At the heart of this craft is the design of 3D integrated circuits. Unlike their 2D counterparts, these circuits use vertical space, leading to denser configurations and enhanced quantum interactions. However, constructing these requires specialized insulators that prevent unwanted interactions and ensure the delicate quantum states aren't easily disturbed.

High-purity silicon is another heavyweight in the quantum arena. Renowned for its consistent and almost pure atomic structure, this material provides a stable foundation for quantum dots. But the real magic lies in achieving and maintaining that purity. Clean interfaces, absent of any contaminating elements, become crucial. Cleaner interfaces reduce the chances of quantum data leakage, ensuring qubits function optimally.

The process of molecular beam epitaxy is pivotal in this scenario. It allows scientists to deposit atomic layers of materials in a highly controlled manner. This precision layering ensures superior insulation and fewer imperfections, providing a controlled environment where qubits can thrive without interference.

It's not enough to just have pure materials; their assembly needs to be precise. The art of quantum material crafting calls for exactness in placing every atom, especially when dealing with metals and crystals. Enhanced fabrication techniques ensure these interfaces, where materials meet, remain uncontaminated, preserving the integrity of the quantum states.

## 10 Milestones Before Mastery

The map of quantum computing, particularly in hardware, is marked by significant achievements. As we navigate this journey, we must highlight the key destinations researchers aim to hit before quantum computers reach their peak performance.

*Qubit Stability & Coherence*

At the heart of quantum computation lies the qubit, a unit that's notably finicky. It must maintain its quantum state, or "coherence", for effective operation. Recent efforts have led to impressive enhancements in the coherence times of superconducting qubits and trapped ions, two vanguards of qubit technologies.

*Navigating the NISQ Waters*

Quantum computing is presently in the Noisy Intermediate-Scale Quantum (NISQ) era. Although these machines are error-prone and lack fault tolerance, they serve as invaluable testing grounds, allowing researchers to refine algorithms, materials, and methodologies.

*Error Management with Quantum Finesse*

The delicate nature of qubits makes them susceptible to errors. To address this, the quantum community is intensely developing quantum error correction methods, with techniques like the surface code designed to maintain quantum states even when mistakes occur.

*The Material Science Vanguard*

Breakthroughs in materials science remain a cornerstone of quantum progress. By exploring new terrains like topological qubits and mysterious Majorana fermions, scientists hope to fix disturbances by crafting both scalable and robust qubits.

## Cryogenics, The Quantum Chiller

Keeping qubits cool and in their quantum state is no small feat. As we plan for quantum systems with an ever-growing number of qubits, innovations in quantum cryogenics, like advanced dilution refrigerators, become paramount to managing heat efficiently.

## Modularity & Quantum Web

A future where multiple small-scale quantum processors unite to form a quantum powerhouse is on the horizon. This modular vision goes hand in hand with the dream of quantum networking, laying the groundwork for a quantum internet.

## Bridging Quantum & Classical

While quantum processors hold the spotlight, they lean heavily on classical systems for control and error mitigation. The interplay and seamless integration between quantum and classical realms remain a priority.

## The Commercial Quantum Race

Giants like IBM, Google, and Intel, as well as emerging startups, are in a sprint, investing in quantum hardware. Milestones like Google's "quantum supremacy" announcement in 2019 underscore the rapid pace of commercial progress. Since Google's announcement, other companies have also claimed to have achieved quantum supremacy. However, the definition of quantum supremacy is still somewhat vague, and there is some debate about whether these other claims are valid.

*Qubit Diversity*

Beyond the popular superconducting qubits and trapped ions, the quantum world buzzes with research on alternatives, from photonic quantum computing to neutral atom qubits and silicon quantum dots. This diversity promises multiple paths to quantum mastery.

*The Scaling Imperative*

The allure of boosting qubit count is undeniable, but quantity alone doesn't win the race. The connectivity, error rate, and overall quality of these qubits remain equally, if not more, vital.

Each of these milestones, while serving as markers of progress, also paves the way for deeper exploration into the very fabric of our universe. In the next section, we'll explore how quantum principles apply at the molecular level.

## Molecular Quantum Mechanics

Quantum chemistry plays a significant role in understanding and designing materials for quantum computers. Here's how:

1.   **Foundational Understanding**: At its core, quantum chemistry deals with the quantum mechanical behavior of electrons in atoms and molecules. This understanding is essential for predicting how matter behaves at the quantum level, especially when considering raw materials for qubits or other quantum systems.

2.   **Designing New Materials**: Quantum chemistry simulations can guide the creation of novel materials with specific electronic or magnetic properties tailored for quantum computation. By

understanding how electrons interact in a given material, scientists can engineer new tools with desirable quantum computing properties, such as longer coherence times.

3. **Superconductivity**: Many quantum computers rely on superconducting qubits. Quantum chemistry provides insight into the pairing mechanisms of electrons in superconductors, which is crucial for designing better superconducting elements suitable for quantum computation.

4. **Quantum Dots**: As mentioned before, quantum dots are semiconductor nanocrystals that exhibit quantum mechanical properties. Quantum chemistry offers insights into the electronic structures of these dots, influencing their design and implementation in quantum systems.

5. **Interaction with Environment**: One of the challenges in quantum computing is the interaction of qubits with their environment, leading to decoherence. Chemists can model and predict these interactions, helping in the design of materials that minimize such unwanted interactions.

6. **Optimizing Interfaces**: For solid-state quantum systems, the interfaces between different materials can be sites of noise and loss. Quantum chemistry can model these interfaces, guiding the selection and design of materials to minimize these issues.

Quantum chemistry bridges the abstract practical domain of material science. By simulating and predicting the quantum behaviors of materials, quantum chemists help strive for the optimization and innovation of futuristic computers.

The convergence of improved materials, innovative architectures, and advanced engineering solutions paints a promising picture for quantum computing's future. The next frontier involves not just the development of larger quantum systems but ensuring they are robust, interconnected, and geared for real-world applications. No computer is complete without software! Software is undeniably a critical part of the quantum computing ecosystem. It dictates how we utilize and maximize the potential of the hardware.

## Quantum Software

*The Code Behind the Quantum Leap*

As quantum hardware matures, the software unleashes its full potential. Without sophisticated software frameworks, even the most advanced quantum computer would lack a powerful engine to channel its energy.

1. **Quantum Algorithms**: At the heart of quantum software are quantum algorithms, which leverage quantum phenomena to process information in ways unattainable for classical computers. Algorithms like Shor's for factoring or Grover's for search promise computational speeds that classical counterparts can't match.

2. **Programming Languages**: Just as classical computers have C++, Java, or Python, the quantum world has seen the emergence of specialized languages. Q# from Microsoft and QuTiP are just a few examples tailored to describe quantum processes and operations.

3. **Quantum Compilers**: Transforming quantum code into operations that a quantum chip can understand is no small task.

Quantum translations need to be far more sophisticated, considering the nuances of quantum physics and the unique architecture of quantum processors.

4. **Noise and Error Mitigation**: While hardware researchers focus on error correction at the physical level, software plays a crucial role, too. Algorithms are being developed to either be powerful against noise or compensate for the errors introduced during computation.

5. **Hybrid Systems**: Given that full-scale, error-corrected quantum computers are still on the horizon, much of today's work revolves around hybrid systems. These combine the strengths of classical and quantum computers, enabling solutions to problems like optimization or simulations that leverage the best of both worlds.

6. **Quantum Software Platforms**: Major tech entities and startups offer platforms where quantum algorithms can be tested and refined. IBM's Qiskit or Google's Cirq provide open-source tools for budding quantum programmers to experiment, learn, and innovate.

7. **Quantum Simulators**: Before running algorithms on real quantum hardware, they are often tested on quantum simulators. These software tools mimic the behavior of quantum systems, allowing for debugging and optimization in a controlled environment.

8. **Applications and Industries**: Quantum software's final frontier is actual applications. From cryptography to drug discovery, the potential domains that can benefit from quantum computation are

vast. Each application demands its own set of specialized software tools and algorithms.

Quantum software is the bridge that translates theoretical quantum advantages into real-world outcomes. As the hardware landscape evolves, so will the software ecosystem, ensuring that when quantum computers are ready for mainstream use, the tools to harness their power will be well-refined and poised for evolution.

## Quantum Software vs. Classical Software

- **Nature of Operations**: Classical software operates on bits. Quantum software must account for qubits in a superposition of states and entangled with other qubits. This fundamental difference has a lot of upsides but comes with challenges.

- **Algorithm Complexity**: While classical algorithms follow deterministic logic (given the same input, you'll always have the same output), quantum algorithms work probabilistically. You might run a quantum algorithm multiple times to get a probable correct answer.

- **Error Handling**: Classical computers deal with errors, but digital error correction is well-understood and manageable. In quantum computing, error correction is far more challenging due to the delicate nature of qubits and their vulnerability to external influences. Quantum software must either be robust against these errors or work with hardware-level error correction.

- **Programming Paradigm**: Quantum programming often requires a shift in mindset. While classical programming can be very linear, quantum programming requires an understanding of quantum mechanics' language.

## Software-Hardware Interface

- **Hardware Abstraction**: Just as classical software often uses drivers and other concepts to communicate with a variety of hardware, quantum software needs to do the same. Given the variety of quantum hardware (superconducting qubits, trapped ions, topological qubits, etc.), software platforms aim to provide a unified interface for programmers.

- **Hardware-Specific Optimizations**: Quantum compilers play a crucial role. They translate high-level quantum algorithms (programming code) into machine-readable instructions specific to the hardware of the quantum processor's unique architecture and constraints. Ultimately enabling the execution of programs on the computer.

- **Feedback Loop**: The development of quantum hardware and software is reciprocal. Insights gained from software experiments can guide hardware improvements, and advancements in hardware can open up new possibilities for software.

- **Hybrid Systems**: Current quantum systems often work in collaboration with classical systems. Quantum software typically involves a mix where the quantum computer handles specific tasks that leverage its strengths, while classical systems manage other tasks. This collaboration requires software to efficiently communicate and distribute tasks between the two.

- **Ecosystem Collaboration**: Many quantum startups and tech giants are not just building quantum computers but complete quantum systems - combining hardware, software, and often cloud-based platforms for users to access quantum resources. The broader ecosystem recognizes the cohesive nature of hardware and software, pushing advancements in tandem to ensure that as quantum computers become more powerful, the tools to harness them keep pace.

While classical software has matured over decades, quantum software is still in its early stages. Yet, its rapid evolution, driven by unique challenges and opportunities, sets the stage for computational dominance.

## Driving Quantum Computing Forward

The quantum computing ecosystem is broad and includes diverse players ranging from tech giants to startups, research institutions, and more.

1.   **Tech Giants**: These are industry leaders with extensive resources, continually pushing the boundaries in quantum research. For instance, IBM emphasizes the creation of an open community

as fundamental for the future of quantum computing. Their efforts in the field underscore the importance of collaboration and open-source principles.

2.   **Startups**: Young and agile startups bring fresh perspectives to the table. They're mainly focused on making quantum computing practical and scalable, working diligently to transition quantum technologies into usable applications.

3.   **Research Institutions**: Universities and labs globally champion quantum research. The US, for instance, stands out as a leading player in quantum tech research and investment. These institutions often collaborate with tech giants and startups, fostering a cohesive environment for advancement.

4.   **Government and Public Entities**: Quantum technology is increasingly recognized as the next big thing. Countries and public institutions worldwide are investing in research and formulating policies to support the ecosystem's growth.

As the quantum ecosystem continues to expand, openness, partnerships, and investments from these entities will be essential in realizing the potential of quantum computing in industries such as pharmaceuticals, chemicals, automotive, and finance (see Chapter Five).

## Ecosystem Expands in All Directions

Quantum computers are rapidly evolving thanks to multifaceted collaborations, pioneering research initiatives, and key investment strategies. As this technology promises to transform various sectors, understanding the main drivers behind its progress becomes crucial. A closer look at the quantum ecosystem reveals how these collective efforts, whether through research, strategic alliances, or funding surges, turbocharge quantum computing in a big way.

1.   **Collaborative Research:** Quantum advancements have been supported by platforms like Classiq, which enable the effective creation and execution of quantum algorithms, addressing real-world use cases. Additionally, academic institutions, such as UC Santa Barbara, have forged collaborations with tech giants like Cisco Systems to push quantum technology forward.

2.   **Investment Activities:** A testament to the thriving interest in quantum technology is the rise of numerous quantum computing companies. Private investment in quantum technology reached a record high of $2.35 billion in 2022. Some of that went to IonQ, which raised $450 million; Rigetti raised $300 million, and PsiQuantum raised $450 million. That's only a few of the 90-plus companies currently raising money.

3.   **Strategic Partnerships:** The quantum ecosystem is not limited to research labs but has extended to corporate boardrooms. This evolution signifies the birth of new hardware, software, and crucial partnerships that aim to accelerate quantum computing's practical applications.

4.   **Public-Private Initiatives:** While not explicitly stated in the search results, public-private collaborations, like the one between UC Santa Barbara and Cisco Systems, serve as examples of how

governments and private entities are joining forces to further quantum research and its applications.

The transformative power of quantum computing hinges on technological advancements and the synergetic collaborations and investments underpinning its growth. The unified commitment towards exploring and unlocking quantum potential is clear from academia to corporate giants. This holistic approach in research, partnerships, and public-private initiatives is foundational in steering quantum computing's trajectory from aspiration to actualization.

Whether you know it or not, your company might already be tapping into quantum systems. If you're an entrepreneur, perhaps you've ventured into the world of quantum simulators, harnessing their computational might for your projects. The quantum revolution is not just on the horizon; it's already merging with our professional landscapes. As we advance, let's shift our focus to Quantum Simulation, revealing how it's developing our understanding of complex systems.

## The Power and Practice of Quantum Simulation

Whether you're a cutting-edge researcher, industry innovator, or an enthusiast, step into the quantum simulator. At its core, a quantum simulator is a specialized computer designed to mimic and predict the behavior of quantum systems. This tool is a testament to the advancements in the field, bridging the abstract world of quantum mechanics with practical applications.

But what makes a quantum simulator so unique? It operates using qubits, the fundamental units of quantum information. While early simulators were celebrated for merely utilizing a handful of qubits, technology's relentless march forward now sees devices wielding anywhere from a few to nearly a thousand qubits. However, it's essential to remember that the game isn't solely about stockpiling qubits. The quality of these qubits, including aspects like their error rates, coherence times, and connectivity, plays a pivotal role in the simulator's efficacy. In some scenarios, a simulator with fewer but higher-quality qubits can outshine one boasting a greater amount but of lesser integrity.

Understanding quantum simulators means appreciating both their complexity and their potential. They are the looking glass into quantum phenomena, enabling scientists to decipher intricate quantum behaviors without having to observe them directly in nature. As we look into this section, you'll discover the applications of these powerful devices in various industries.

Quantum simulation plays a pivotal role in numerous industries:

1. **Energy Applications**: Quantum simulations will help us understand complex energy systems. They're being leveraged to optimize and find efficient energy solutions, from advancing solar cells to understanding nuclear fusion processes.

2. **Chemistry**: The molecular world is rife with complexity. Quantum simulators provide unparalleled precision in simulating chemical reactions, which is of significant value in areas like drug discovery and material science. For instance, Peter Morgan

showcased the potential of quantum computers in simulating chemical reactions to drive advancements in these sectors.

3.  **Material Science**: Quantum simulations can probe the properties of new materials at the quantum level, facilitating the discovery of novel substances with desired properties, from superconductors to efficient insulators.

4.  **Business and Financial Modeling**: Quantum simulators can handle complex financial models, optimize portfolios, and manage risk with higher precision.

5.  **Advanced Chemical Reactions**: In the field of electric vehicles (EVs), quantum simulations play a part in understanding and optimizing battery chemistry, holding the potential to revolutionize the EV industry.

These applications signify just the beginning of what's possible. Their efficacy, however, is deeply entangled with the algorithms and techniques employed. Let's explore the complexities of the 'Algorithms and Techniques for Quantum Simulation' to further grasp how these simulations achieve their remarkable results.

The algorithms and techniques underlying quantum simulation are intricate and aimed at mimicking quantum phenomena that classical systems can't efficiently handle. Here are some core techniques:

*Basic Quantum Algorithms*

The foundational algorithms in quantum computing provide the bedrock for advanced simulations. Such algorithms include quantum Fourier transform and phase estimation, often serving as building blocks for more complex simulation tasks.

*Variational Quantum Eigensolver (VQE)*

VQE is a hybrid algorithm that optimizes quantum circuit parameters to approximate a quantum system's ground state energy. It has the advantage of being executable on near-term quantum devices, making it valuable for tackling optimization problems.

*Polynomial-time Quantum Algorithms*

Traditional simulations on classical computers can exponentially increase computational costs as the quantum system size increases. However, specific quantum algorithms have been designed for simulations, achieving polynomial time complexities.

*Simulating Dynamical Quantum Phases*

Techniques such as the sequential quantum circuit on superconducting quantum devices are optimized to simulate specific quantum states, like ground states, highlighting the flexibility and adaptability of quantum simulators.

As quantum technology advances, we'll see even more sophisticated techniques emerge, further blurring the lines between the quantum domain and our digital computational capabilities.

Utilizing a quantum simulator allows you to harness quantum effects to probe questions about model systems, which in turn can shed light on real-world scenarios. To use a quantum simulator effectively:

*Understand the Basics*

Grasp the fundamental concepts of quantum mechanics and how quantum simulators differ from traditional quantum computers. Quantum simulators are designed to mimic specific quantum systems that might be difficult to study directly.

*Choose the Right Platform*

Various platforms, like Google Cloud, offer tools for quantum simulation. For instance, Google Cloud provides a tutorial on simulating a quantum circuit using Cirq and qsim.

*Install Necessary Tools*

Depending on the platform, you might need to install specific software or packages. For instance, with Google's tutorial, you'd learn how to install Cirq and set up qsim.

*Study Existing Models*

Dive deep into theoretical and experimental development of quantum simulation using quantum computers to understand established techniques and methodologies.

*Push the Boundaries*

As quantum technology evolves, new phenomena are being discovered, such as entirely new phases of matter simulated using quantum computers. By staying updated, you can harness the full potential of quantum simulation.

As the curtain of this chapter draws to a close, it's crucial to underscore the dynamic nature of the quantum world. The quantum computing and simulation field is not static; it's like a river, continuously flowing and changing its course. Every day, new developments emerge, paradigms shift, and what we believed was once the frontier becomes the new standard.

To aid your journey and help you navigate these rapid waters, I've compiled a resource you'll find invaluable: the "Quantum Toolbox." (Chapter 6). This is not just a list; it's a compass. You'll discover a comprehensive list of quantum simulators within its digital confines and explore practical applications. But the toolbox doesn't stop there. It also directs you to the most insightful online courses available, helping beginners and seasoned quantum enthusiasts expand their knowledge and hone their skills.

With the Quantum Toolbox at your fingertips, you can confidently navigate the quantum domain. But as you proceed, it's equally essential to clear the haze surrounding quantum computing. Over time, misconceptions, myths, and misunderstandings have weaved a web of confusion for many. But worry not, for our next chapter aims to untangle this web.

The next chapter, *Dispelling Common Misconceptions of Quantum Computing*, promises to debunk myths, clarify confusions, and set the record straight. Together, we'll scrutinize common misunderstandings, ensuring you're knowledgeable and accurate in your quantum pursuits.

# CHAPTER 3

## DISPELLING QUANTUM MISCONCEPTIONS

### Unmasking Illusions in the Enchanted Forest

Welcome, brave explorer, to the Enchanted Forest of Quantum Computing—a world shrouded in both reality and myth. Walking through the twisted groves of qubits and quantum gates makes it easy to be hypnotized by the whispers of instant computational power or universal encryption-breaking abilities. However, much like any enchanted forest, not all that glitters is gold, and not all tales told are true.

This chapter aims to light a path through this dense bush of misunderstanding. With each step, we'll unmask the illusions that have cast a shadow over the actual potentials and limitations of quantum computing. Armed with the truth, you'll emerge from the forest not just enchanted but enlightened.

Prepare to investigate ten of the biggest misconceptions about this mystical domain. Along the way, you'll gain a balanced perspective on what quantum computers can and can't do, and dispel some common myths surrounding their speed, utility, and complexity.

Ready your lanterns and sharpen your mental machetes; we're about to debunk some illusions and reveal the genuine magic of quantum computing.

## Quantum Technology is Mainstream

In our Enchanted Forest of Quantum Computing, many adventurers have heard whispers of a mystical waterfall that grants wisdom and untold power—much like the widespread belief that quantum technology is as mainstream as the smartphones in our pockets.

Yet, like the mainstream status of quantum technology, the waterfall is not as prominent as it appears. While there have been substantial advancements, the majority of quantum computing applications remain experimental. The few areas with practical use are specialized, primarily in research labs or specific industrial sectors.

Believing that quantum technology is already mainstream can create inflated expectations and potentially lead to poor decision-making. Companies may prematurely invest in quantum computing, and individuals may mistakenly think they need an immediate understanding of quantum principles for career advancement.

Imagine walking through the forest, captivated by the shimmering mirage of a waterfall up ahead. As you approach, the mirage dissipates into mist, thirsty for its promised power. This evaporation reflects the fading allure of the mainstream status of quantum technology upon closer scrutiny.

Quantum technology is undeniably promising and is making strides toward broader applicability. However, it's crucial to understand that it's still primarily a technology of the future, not the present.

## Quantum Computers are Only for Academic Research

Touring further into our Enchanted Forest of Quantum Computing, you might encounter trails that are rumored to lead nowhere, much like the illusion that quantum computers serve only the arcane interests of academia.

Many explorers believe these "useless" trails are worth skipping in favor of more traveled paths, just as some people think quantum computers are only accessible to academic institutions, with no relevance in the free world of open source.

As it turns out, these hidden trails may lead to unseen treasure troves. Quantum computing isn't just for academic research. It has potential applications in various industries like pharmaceuticals for drug discovery, finance for optimization problems, and climate modeling.

The utility of quantum computing extends far beyond the university. While the technology is indeed prominent in research, its potential for real-world impact is too substantial to ignore. Venture capitalists, large corporations, and startups are increasingly investing in quantum computing for practical applications.

Picture walking past a hidden trail, convinced it's a dead-end, only to learn later that it led to a treasure trove of valuable resources. Ignoring the potential applications of quantum computing outside academia is similar; you might miss out on a wealth of opportunities.

Quantum computing is not confined to the ivory towers of suit coats and academia. It has a burgeoning role in solving everyday problems and offers a landscape of untapped potential.

As we leave behind the hidden trails filled with untold riches, we prepare to navigate another twist in our journey. The myth that quantum computing and blockchain are like oil and water—entirely incompatible.

## Trees of Different Species Coexisting in the Forest

As we tread deeper into the Enchanted Forest, let's stop for a moment at the forest clearing where two different species of trees seem to grow in tension—much like the misconception that quantum computing and blockchain technologies are fundamentally at odds.

Many adventurers of the quantum realm believe that the rise of quantum computing spells doom for blockchain technologies. The fear is that quantum computers could easily break the cryptographic foundations that secure blockchain, rendering it obsolete.

It's essential to recognize that while quantum computing poses a challenge to current cryptographic techniques, blockchain is not a static technology. Already, there are ongoing efforts to develop quantum-resistant cryptographic algorithms, ensuring that blockchain can adapt and coexist with quantum computing.

The relationship between quantum computing and blockchain is not a zero-sum game. The advent of quantum computing will likely prompt a cryptographic evolution, making blockchain technologies even more secure and robust.

Imagine two distinct species of trees in the forest. At first glance, they seem to vie for the same resources, but a closer look reveals a balanced ecosystem where both can thrive. Quantum computing and blockchain are like these trees: they may seem incompatible, but they can coexist, each making its unique contributions to the forest—or, in this case, the digital world.

Blockchain and quantum computing are not enemies but can evolve to coexist, complementing each other in enhancing security and performance in the digital realm.

As we admire the diverse foliage of our enchanted forest, let's prepare for the next leg of our journey. We will venture into the area shrouded by the misconception that quantum computers will completely replace classical computers—a belief that could misguide our understanding of both domains.

## Different Tools in an Explorer's Toolkit

As we trek further into the depths of our mystical forest, our explorer's toolkit comes into focus. Imagine hearing whispers that a new, magical tool is so powerful that it will render all other gadgets obsolete. This mirrors the myth that quantum computers will make classical computing a relic of the past—a prevailing notion among enchanted wanderers and tech enthusiasts alike.

Many envision a future where our current computers gather dust in attics, overshadowed by the dazzling might of quantum machines.

It's crucial to understand that quantum and classical computers serve different but complementary purposes. Quantum computing excels at specific types of problems—like optimization and factorization—but classical computers are more efficient and practical for many of our everyday tasks.

In the broader landscape of computational challenges, classical and quantum computing can work in symbiosis. Many advanced quantum algorithms, for instance, require a classical computer for pre-processing and post-processing tasks. Far from making classical computers obsolete, quantum computers will likely augment their capabilities.

Think of your explorer's toolkit. You wouldn't use a compass to cut through vines or rely solely on a machete to navigate your path. Similarly, quantum and classical computers are like different tools in your gear, each excelling in its specific role.

We are confident that quantum computers aren't destined to replace classical computers but will work alongside them to solve problems neither could tackle alone.

Having expanded our toolkit and dispelled the illusion that one tool could do it all, let's continue our expedition. Our next destination? A mysterious area in the forest shrouded by the belief that you need a Ph.D. in quantum physics to touch a quantum computer.

## Do You Need a Ph.D. to Speak the Language?

As we continue our adventure, we encounter a stone tablet with complex inscriptions that might as well be hieroglyphics. Rumor has it that only those with doctorates in quantum physics can decipher these symbols. There is a foggy landscape of misconception that you need to be an expert in quantum physics to begin understanding or even using quantum computers.

A pervasive myth exists that quantum computing is an exclusive club, only accessible to those who have mastered the complexities of quantum mechanics. This daunting belief puts an imaginary barrier around quantum computing, making it seem as unapproachable as an ancient riddle.

Contrary to the intimidating climate surrounding it, quantum computing is becoming increasingly user-friendly. With the advent of high-level programming languages and libraries designed specifically for quantum computing, like Qiskit, Quipper, and Microsoft's Q#, the field is more accessible than ever.

While a quantum physics background can certainly deepen your understanding, it's no longer a strict prerequisite. You don't need to be fluent in the intricate math behind quantum mechanics to use or even program a quantum computer. Similar to learning any other programming language, dedication and practice can get you far.

Imagine stumbling upon a stone tablet with a seemingly indecipherable code. However, as you approach, the code magically transforms into simple phrases. Similarly, the complex math behind quantum computing is getting 'translated' into approachable language through user-friendly tools and platforms.

Don't be deterred by the complexity of quantum mechanics; advances in quantum computing are bringing the field within reach for a broader audience.

Having successfully deciphered the 'quantum language,' we realize that this Enchanted Forest is accessible to many, not just a select few scholars. And now, we turn our attention to another dark corner of the forest—a place where quantum computing is deemed too complex for the average person to grasp.

## Can You Solve This Puzzle?

A thick fog envelops us as we journey deeper into the Enchanted Forest. Our surroundings become hazy and difficult to make out, mirroring the perception that quantum computing is only suited for the minds of geniuses.

Many believe that understanding quantum computing is like cracking a cryptic code: almost impossible unless you're a genius in math and physics. The notion is that quantum computing is so complex it's out of reach for ordinary people.

The fog may feel overpowering, but it isn't. Simple concepts like superposition (being in multiple states at once) and entanglement (particles affecting each other regardless of distance) are at the core of quantum mechanics. Yes, the math behind it is complex, but you don't need to master it to appreciate the fundamental principles.

Understanding quantum computing doesn't require plunging into wave equations or matrix algebra. Many universities and online platforms offer introductory courses to quantum computing that require no more than a high school understanding of math and science.

As we navigate through the fog, it suddenly lifts, revealing a beautiful landscape full of life and discovery. The once impenetrable haze was just a passing phase, much like the initial intimidation one might feel when approaching quantum computing. It looks difficult at first glance, but it's possible to grasp its basic principles without being a genius or a quantum physicist. The complexity burns away as you continue to understand.

We've moved past the haze and find ourselves eager to explore more of what this forest has to offer. Similarly, the initial complexity of quantum computing starts to make sense as we chop through the thick foliage. But beware, the next trail leads us to the castle of cryptography—a place where many believe quantum computing holds the keys to every locked door.

## The Fallacy of Immortal Decryption

As we traverse deeper into the Enchanted Forest, we come upon a secretive castle of cryptography. Whispers among travelers suggest that a powerful sorcerer resides here, wielding the power to unlock any enchanted seal or guarded door. This fable parallels the fear that quantum computers will one day break all forms of encryption, exposing our data and secrets completely.

The myth goes like this: once quantum computers are advanced enough, they will crack open all existing encryption algorithms, making all security measures obsolete overnight. Your online banking, sensitive emails, and even national security secrets would be revealed.

Before you start guarding your secrets even more anxiously, it's essential to know that cryptographers are already on the case. They're developing quantum-resistant algorithms that even the most potent quantum "sorcerer" will find challenging to break. Even if quantum computers could, theoretically, break some existing encryption methods like RSA, they won't make all forms of encryption obsolete.

The cryptographic world is in a dynamic transformation with the development of quantum computing. As quantum computers inch closer to breaking certain encryption types, cryptography is evolving to stay ahead, ensuring a future where they ethically coexist.

In the forest, the "sorcerer" is not invincible but rather a balanced part of the ecosystem. While he may have the skills to break simpler charms and spells, the forest is also home to enchantresses and wise sages developing even stronger magic to counterbalance his power. Ensuring harmony and balance are maintained in this ever-evolving landscape.

Leaving the castle, we understand that no single entity—be it a sorcerer or a quantum computer—holds absolute power in the Enchanted Forest or the world of encryption. As we migrate to the next corner of the forest, we'll explore another popular myth—that all algorithms run faster on quantum computers.

# Quantum Isn't Always Quicker

Navigating through the Enchanted Forest, we come upon a stream with an unusual reputation—it's said to make anyone who swims in it instantly faster. The misconception is that all algorithms will run faster if executed on a quantum computer. The allure of "speed" can make this stream seem like a universal solution to all of our problems.

The general perception is that quantum computers, by their very nature, will speed up any algorithm you throw at them. Need to sort a list? A quantum computer will do it faster. Want to find the shortest path in a network? Surely, a quantum computer is quicker. This myth suggests that quantum computing is a turbo-button for all computational tasks.

While it's true that quantum computers show exceptional speed for specific problems—like integer factorization or searching unsorted databases—their speed-up is problem-specific. For many traditional algorithms, a classical computer is as fast, or even faster, and far less resource-intensive.

Quantum computers excel at solving inherently quantum problems or can be effectively mapped onto a quantum framework. Their advantage is not universal but instead confined to certain kinds of troubles. Knowing this helps focus research and investment into quantum computing, where it can offer the most benefit. It's not a panacea for all slow-moving features but offers its gifts selectively.

As we leave the mystical stream behind, we find ourselves asking the overarching question: "Are quantum computers genuinely fast"?

This will be the focus of our next observation in the Enchanted Forest of Quantum Computing.

## Are Quantum Computers Crazy Fast?

As we hike deeper into the Enchanted Forest of Quantum Computing, we encounter tales of the Swiftfoot—a mythical creature famous for outrunning the wind itself. The legend of Swiftfoot is not unlike the widespread belief that quantum computers are universally faster than their classical counterparts.

The invasive myth is that quantum computers, equipped with superposition and entanglement, can solve any problem faster than classical computers. In this view, a quantum computer is like a super-charged engine that will blaze through every computational race.

While quantum computers do possess certain speed advantages, these advantages are conditional. Quantum algorithms like Shor's and Grover's offer exponentially faster solutions to specific problems, such as integer factorization or unsorted database searching. However, classical computers still hold their ground for many routine tasks and algorithms.

It's critical to understand that quantum computers generally aren't 'faster'. They are faster at specific tasks that are inherently suited for quantum computation. This specialty makes them invaluable for some complex issues but not a universal replacement for classical computing speed.

Upon tracking the elusive Swiftfoot, we find that its legendary speed isn't constant. It only displays its breathtaking swiftness when the stars align or when chasing particular prey. Recognizing this can help us align our focus during research and development.

As we bid farewell to the mystical Swiftfoot, our next quest awaits. It involves an even more enigmatic and misunderstood notion: the idea that quantum computers operate in multiple universes. Let's tread lightly as we approach this next layer of quantum mythology.

## The Guardian of Many Worlds

Ah, at last, we arrive at the heart of the Enchanted Forest to confront the elusive "Guardian," a creature said to exist in not just this realm but many others. Just like this mythical being, quantum computers are often believed to operate across multiple universes—a concept that captures our imagination but distorts our understanding.

Many envision quantum computers as magical devices that tap into parallel universes to perform their computations. This popular belief is inspired by the Many-Worlds Interpretation (MWI) of quantum mechanics, which is often misunderstood or oversimplified.

While MWI is a legitimate interpretation of quantum mechanics, it's critical to understand that it is not the only interpretation, nor is it universally accepted. More importantly, you don't need multiple universes to explain how quantum computers work. They operate based on superposition and entanglement, well-understood principles within our own "universe."

As enticing as it is to consider quantum computing a byproduct of multiple universes, it's essential to ground this technological marvel in the scientific framework that birthed it. Understanding quantum computers within the boundaries of our current scientific knowledge keeps us from veering into the realm of science fiction.

When finally encountered, the Guardian turns out to be a wise old tree. Its roots don't stretch into other worlds, but its branches provide shelter and wisdom in this one. Similarly, quantum computing doesn't require an alliance with parallel universes to manifest its incredible capabilities.

As we part ways with the Guardian, the mythical and the mystical begin to blur into the mist of the forest. But the path to understanding quantum computing continues to stretch beyond the horizon. Are you ready for what comes next? Your newfound clarity will surely make the journey less treacherous and far more enlightening.

## Emerging from the Enchanted Forest, Enlightened

Our adventure through the Enchanted Forest of Quantum Computing has been transformative, abundant with revelations and unexpected turns. We've debunked some deeply rooted misconceptions—from the idea that quantum technology is already mainstream, to the mysterious notion that it operates across multiple universes. Along the way, we've not only dispelled illusions but also shone a light on the genuinely enchanting qualities of this groundbreaking technology.

*Key Takeaways*

1. **Quantum technology is in its infancy**—it's not yet mainstream but has real-world applications.

2. **Beyond academia**—quantum computing has the potential to revolutionize various industries.

3. **Compatibility with existing technology**—quantum computing can co-exist with technologies like blockchain.

4. **Complement, not replace**—quantum and classical computers serve different, complementary roles.

5. **Accessible to many**—you don't need to be a physicist to use or understand quantum computing.

6. **Democratization of understanding**—quantum computing is not too complex for laypeople to grasp.

7. **Encryption Evolution**—quantum computers pose challenges but also drive cryptographic innovation.

8. **Niche advantages**—quantum computing offers specific speed-ups, not universal ones.

9. **Speed is Relative**—quantum computers excel at particular tasks but are not universally faster.

10. **Single Universe Understanding**—quantum computing can be explained within our known physical laws.

Understanding quantum computing—the more you explore, the more you realize there is to discover. So, let this chapter not be an endpoint but a stepping stone in your ongoing quest for understanding this revolutionary technology.

## Next Chapter

*Quantum Algorithmic Treasures—Unlocking the Cryptographic Caves*

If you've enjoyed this journey through the Enchanted Forest, the exploration is far from over. Next, we're diving into the intricate world of Quantum Algorithmic Treasures. Here, we'll unlock the Cryptographic Caves where the promise of quantum computing holds the keys to unprecedented computational wonders. Are you ready to start the next quest? The Cryptographic Caves await your arrival, and their secrets are begging to be unearthed.

Armed with your new understanding and free of misconceptions, the path ahead is clear. The forest may still be enchanted, but you, brave explorer, are now enlightened. Onward to the Cryptographic Caves!

## Bonus

*Quantum Computers and AI Will Take Over the World*

Many of us have been enchanted by science fiction tales where highly intelligent machines become sentient and decide to overthrow humanity. Throw quantum computing into the mix, and you have a recipe for a gripping apocalyptic narrative. The misconception is that combining quantum computing and artificial intelligence will inevitably lead to a future where machines rule, and humans are downgraded to secondary roles—or worse.

Quantum computers, given their immense computational powers, coupled with the learning capabilities of AI, will evolve beyond human control, leading to a "Judgment Day" scenario.

While it's true that quantum computing can potentially revolutionize AI, making it more efficient and capable, it's crucial to remember that both technologies are tools created and controlled by humans. Ethical guidelines, governance, and safety precautions are all areas of active research aimed at ensuring that these technologies are developed responsibly.

Quantum computing will likely advance AI, but it won't make AI inherently evil or uncontrollable. Ethical use of technology depends on human choices and societal values, not just the capabilities of the technology itself. Moreover, practical and theoretical limitations (e.g., error rates in quantum computing and energy requirements) provide natural checks on runaway scenarios.

Imagine stumbling upon a powerful wizard and a mighty dragon having a meeting deep within the Enchanted Forest. The wizard represents quantum computing, and the dragon symbolizes AI. Together, they have the power to either protect the forest or plunge it into chaos. Yet, they are bound by ancient spells and forest laws that prevent them from acting recklessly. These spells and laws are the ethical guidelines and regulations we place on technology.

The combination of quantum computing and AI is indeed powerful but not apocalyptic. Through responsible development and governance, we can channel their strengths for the betterment of humanity, rather than our downfall.

You can tell that we here at Pantheon Space Academy are AI optimists. I hope you enjoyed the 11 misconceptions, topped off with the Hollywood-worthy notion of AI and quantum computing taking over the world. This misconception, like the others, unravels under scrutiny. As we move forward, the real magic lies in using these incredible technologies responsibly, unlocking their potential without succumbing to imagined fears.

# CHAPTER 4

## QUANTUM ALGORITHMS

### Introduction to Quantum Algorithms and their Unique Characteristics

Like seasoned explorers about to embark on an epic adventure into the unknown, we find ourselves at the mouth of the Cryptographic Caves, ready to enter the captivating world of quantum algorithms. Math might seem too complex, but with the right mindset and teacher, it is actually an exciting quest for the rarest of treasures, treasures that have the potential to fundamentally reshape the digital landscape we know today.

Quantum algorithms, the metaphorical keys that unlock the hidden depths of these caves, are a rich blend of physics, mathematics, and computer science. They are not mere replacements for their classical counterparts, but rather, they constitute an entirely different level of solutions, one which exploits the fascinating principles of quantum mechanics - superposition, entanglement, and quantum interference - to solve problems that are computationally challenging, if not impossible for classical computers.

These algorithms are unique in their ability to perform complex tasks more efficiently than classical methods. For instance, Shor's algorithm, one of the gems we shall encounter on our journey, can easily factorize large numbers that dwarf the most effective classical machines. Grover's algorithm, another absolute jewel within the caves, offers a speedier search method in unsorted databases.

While these treasures may dazzle with brilliance, it's essential to remember that their true worth lies not merely in their novelty but in their transformative impact on various fields. From cryptography, where quantum algorithms can potentially break modern encryption systems, to optimization, where they promise superior solutions to complex problems, these treasures are poised to revolutionize our technological ecosystem.

As we hike further into this chapter, we will seek to understand these quantum algorithms, their unique characteristics, and their real-world applications. With each step we take, we hope to illuminate these complex concepts, making the quantum dimension an accessible and enlightening space for you.

Turn your headlamps on, fellow explorers. The adventure begins now, and the Cryptographic Caves are waiting to share their secrets!

## The Forces Behind Quantum Algorithms

As we hike into our cryptographic cave, we need to understand the architects of these caves, the tools they employ, and the computational magic they use to devise these marvelous structures. Quantum algorithms aren't invented in isolation. They are a culmination of centuries of mathematical, computational, and scientific knowledge built by pioneers who dared to defy conventional boundaries.

## The Architects

The world of quantum computing has its heroes. Peter Shor, for instance, who devised Shor's algorithm, set the foundation of quantum cryptography by demonstrating how quantum computers could potentially crack public-key cryptographic systems. Lov Grover, another notable figure, introduced Grover's Algorithm, revolutionizing the field of search algorithms and optimization problems.

Yet, it's not just individuals; teams of scientists, mathematicians, and computer engineers across the globe in academic and industrial settings contribute to this vibrant and dynamic field.

## The Tools

Now, imagine these architects as expert masons, skilled in manipulating the basic building blocks of quantum computation - qubits. Qubits are like magical stones in our cryptographic caves that exist in multiple states at once, due to a property known as superposition. Their interconnectedness, termed entanglement, adds another layer of complexity and power.

Alongside qubits, we have quantum gates, the chisels and hammers that shape the qubits' behavior. Quantum gates perform operations on qubits, manipulating their states to execute the steps of a quantum algorithm. Different combinations of gates result in different algorithms, opening distinct sections of our cryptographic cave.

## The Mathematical and Computational Dance

The process of creating a new quantum algorithm is like a dance between mathematics and computational science. It begins with a problem - a cryptographic treasure that we aim to unlock. Mathematicians and theoretical physicists tackle this by exploring the mathematical structures of the problem, looking for patterns, symmetries, and properties that could be leveraged.

For example, Shor identified the period-finding problem hidden within the prime factorization problem and realized that the Fourier Transform - a mathematical tool used in signal processing - could help solve it in the quantum domain. This led to the development of the Quantum Fourier Transform, a central step in Shor's algorithm.

On the other side of the dance, computational physicists and computer scientists work on the practical aspects. They look at the mathematical structures and strategies identified by the mathematicians and design quantum circuits using qubits and quantum gates that can implement these structures. They also handle the computational challenges of running these algorithms on real quantum computers.

## Real-World Implication

Let's consider the recent developments in quantum machine learning. Scientists realized that certain machine learning tasks involve linear algebra problems that quantum computers could solve more efficiently. Theoretical physicists and mathematicians broke down these tasks into their numerical components, identifying quantum versions of familiar machine learning methods. Meanwhile, computational physicists and computer scientists worked on implementing these ideas as quantum circuits that can be run on existing quantum computers.

The result? We're now seeing the first applications of quantum machine learning, leading to AI that can learn from much larger datasets and model much more complex patterns than what's currently possible with classical computers.

Quantum algorithm discovery is an ongoing collaborative effort, powered by the interplay of mathematics, computational science, and quantum physics. Each algorithm is a testament to human ingenuity and a step further into the mesmerizing quantum world.

## Characteristics of Quantum Algorithms

The quest to unlock the treasures of the Cryptographic Caves truly begins when we grasp the fundamental principles that govern the strange and intricate world of quantum algorithms. The quantum rules vastly differ from the classical world we are accustomed to. It's as if we have transcended the known map and set foot in uncharted territory, with landscapes painted by the brushes of quantum principles such as superposition and entanglement.

A quantum algorithm operates by leveraging these foundational principles, crafting a confidential playbook yet holding immense potential for computational breakthroughs. It is like a secret language understood by the qubits, enabling them to collaborate and perform operations far beyond the reach of classical bits.

At the core of this language lie the peculiar quantum gates, the basic building blocks of quantum algorithms. These gates form a distinct vocabulary of quantum operations, manipulating the states of qubits and creating intricate interactions between them. In a typical classical algorithm, the logical gates alter the states of bits deterministically, similar to how flipping a switch would predictably change a light bulb's state from on to off.

However, quantum gates operate differently. They change the quantum states of qubits not in a deterministic but in a probabilistic manner, leading to a vast array of potential outcomes at the end of a quantum computation. As a result, quantum gates do not just transport us from one point to another in the Cryptographic Caves, but they open up an entire range of possible pathways, each leading to a different treasure.

Another cornerstone of quantum algorithms is the process of measurement, which introduces an element of unpredictability. While the operation of quantum gates might prepare a superposition of many possible states, a quantum measurement collapses this superposition into a single state, with the outcome governed by probabilistic rules. It's as if multiple paths in the Cryptographic Caves merge suddenly into a single path at the time of a treasure's discovery.

Furthermore, quantum algorithms harness the power of interference, a concept central to quantum mechanics. Quantum interference allows for the amplification of correct solutions and the cancellation of wrong ones, manipulating probabilities to guide the algorithm toward the correct answer. It's as if, in the Cryptographic

Caves, the sound of steps leading towards the right path echoes louder, while those leading towards dead ends are muted.

The principles of superposition, entanglement, quantum gates, quantum measurement, and quantum interference form the core characteristics of quantum algorithms. They dictate how these algorithms navigate the computational landscape, enabling them to perform tasks with an efficiency that classical algorithms cannot match. However, understanding these principles is only the first step. To truly value the power and potential of quantum algorithms, we need to go deeper into the Cryptographic Caves and explore the famous quantum algorithms. These hidden gems promise to revolutionize computation.

## Concept of Quantum Parallelism

Quantum parallelism is an essential cog in the machinery of quantum algorithms, operating as a guide within the Cryptographic Caves. Its role is often compared to having multiple keys at your disposal, each capable of unlocking different doors simultaneously. This ability to evaluate numerous possibilities in a single step offers quantum algorithms an edge over their classical counterparts.

Quantum parallelism springs from the principle of super-position, where a qubit can exist in a state that is a combination of the base states $|0\rangle$ and $|1\rangle$. This contrasts sharply with classical bits that can only be in one of two states: 0 or 1. Now, suppose we have a string of n qubits. In a classical computer, an n-bit string can represent one of $2^n$ possible combinations at any given time. However, quantum mechanics allows the n-qubit system to simultaneously exist in a superposition of all $2^n$ combinations. This means that a quantum computer can process all these combinations in a single operation. This ability is the essence of quantum parallelism.

To illustrate the power of quantum parallelism, let's consider a simplified real-world example. Suppose you are looking for a specific book in a vast library and don't know which shelf it's on. A classical computer would be like a single librarian who checks each shelf one by one. If there are a million shelves in the library, in the worst case, the librarian would need to check all one million shelves to find the book.

However, suppose we send a million quantum librarians (a nod to our qubits) into the library. Thanks to the property of quantum parallelism, each quantum librarian can check a different shelf at the same time. Consequently, they could theoretically find the book in a single step, a dramatic speedup compared to the classical approach.

Yet, the story of quantum parallelism doesn't end there. A significant caveat arises during the measurement process. When we measure the state of our quantum librarians, quantum mechanics tells us that we'll get just one result, corresponding to one of the librarians and, thus, one of the shelves. This is akin to the wave function collapse in quantum mechanics, which results in obtaining one specific state from a superposition of many possible states.

So, how do quantum algorithms benefit from parallelism if we can only get one result at the end? The secret lies in the intelligent design of quantum algorithms. By using interference, they ensure that the wrong answers cancel out and the correct answer gets amplified. Thus, when we make a measurement, we are much more likely to find the correct answer.

In the grand expedition within the Cryptographic Caves, quantum parallelism is like having an army of explorers at our disposal. Each explorer takes a different path simultaneously, drastically increasing the chances of finding hidden treasures. The correct path echoes louder, guiding us toward the treasures, while the echoes of the wrong paths cancel each other out, helping us avoid unnecessary detours. Quantum parallelism is essential in designing efficient quantum algorithms, contributing to their potential to outperform classical algorithms.

## The Principles of Superposition And Entanglement

Within the grand Cryptographic Caves, superposition and entanglement, two pillars of quantum mechanics, act as distinct, transformative forces that enable quantum algorithms to operate in ways far removed from classical algorithms.

Superposition, the cornerstone of quantum parallelism we explored earlier, enables a qubit to exist in multiple states simultaneously. This grants quantum algorithms the ability to process a multitude of inputs at once. However, the real magic lies in how quantum algorithms harness this property.

Take, for example, the famous quantum algorithm Grover's search algorithm. This algorithm is designed to find an unsorted database's specific entry, and it does so quadratically faster than any classical algorithm. It starts by placing all the qubits in a superposition, effectively preparing every possible answer. Then, through a process called amplitude amplification, Grover's algorithm manipulates the superposition states so that the amplitude (probability) of the correct answer gradually increases while incorrect answers diminish. After repeating this process several times, a measurement will likely yield the proper response. This clever use of superposition and interference of amplitudes highlights how quantum algorithms are uniquely equipped to solve problems efficiently.

If superposition sets multiple paths for the explorers in the Cryptographic Caves, then entanglement choreographs their synchronized dance. Entanglement is a peculiar quantum phenomenon where particles become interlinked, and the state of one immediately influences the state of the other, regardless of the distance separating them. This instantaneous, spooky action at a distance, as Einstein famously dubbed it, equips quantum algorithms with an added layer of complexity and power.

To grasp how entanglement empowers quantum algorithms, let's delve into the world of quantum teleportation, which utilizes entanglement to transfer quantum information from one location to another. The two communicating parties, traditionally called Alice and Bob, share a pair of entangled qubits. Alice wants to send a qubit state to Bob. She performs a specific operation involving her qubit and the qubit she wants to send, then measures both. She sends the results (two classical bits of information) to Bob. Using this information, Bob performs certain operations on his entangled qubit, recreating the original quantum state Alice wanted to send.

The quantum state is, in a sense, teleported from Alice to Bob. This teleportation rests heavily on the eerie entanglement property and is an essential rule in quantum communication and distributed quantum computing.

In our Cryptographic Caves, if the explorers were entangled, any action performed by one explorer would instantly affect the other, regardless of the distance between them. This immediate and coordinated response could expedite the treasure hunt, guiding the explorers to their desired destination with increased efficiency and synchronization.

Through the combined forces of superposition and entanglement, quantum algorithms unlock a realm of possibilities not available in classical algorithms. By manipulating these core quantum phenomena, quantum algorithms can process vast quantities of data simultaneously, implement intricate computations, and potentially solve certain problems more efficiently, promising a future where the treasure trove of the Cryptographic Caves could be fully revealed.

## The Contrast Between Classical and Quantum Algorithms

Classical and quantum algorithms significantly differ in their operation, taking separate paths toward problem-solving due to the unique principles governing quantum physics. Here's an in-depth look at their characteristics and how they translate into different computational strategies.

In classical computing, data is processed deterministically. That is, given a specific input, the output is precisely defined, following an exact sequence of operations. Classical algorithms manipulate bits that exist in one of two definite states - 0 or 1 - and the state of each bit evolves independently of others. Each operation within a classical algorithm handles these bits individually, moving linearly through the computation steps. Essentially, classical algorithms operate under the laws of classical physics, offering predictability and certainty in their outcomes.

Contrastingly, quantum algorithms leverage quantum mechanical phenomena: superposition, entanglement, and quantum interference, creating an entirely different computational paradigm. In a quantum system, the superposition of a quantum bit (qubit) offers a broader computational base.

Superposition plays a crucial role in quantum parallelism, allowing a quantum system to exist in multiple states simultaneously. This leads to a significant shift in algorithm design. For example, a two-qubit system can represent all four possible states (00, 01, 10, and 11) at once. Therefore, quantum algorithms can perform computations on all these states in parallel, enabling the handling of numerous possibilities simultaneously.

Entanglement is another principle that distinguishes quantum algorithms. When qubits become entangled, the state of one qubit is intertwined with another, no matter their distance apart. Any changes to one qubit instantaneously affect the other. Quantum algorithms harness this property to create a high level of coordination among qubits, facilitating complex computations that would be much more challenging or even impossible for classical algorithms.

Additionally, quantum algorithms exploit interference, a quantum mechanical phenomenon where the probability amplitudes of states can add up or cancel each other out. This property allows quantum algorithms to direct computations toward correct answers and away from incorrect ones, offering a level of computational efficiency beyond the scope of classical algorithms.

These unique quantum principles translate into different efficiencies for various computational tasks. Quantum algorithms, like Shor's algorithm, can factor large numbers with polynomial time complexity, while the best-known classical algorithms require exponential time. This example is an instance of quantum speedup. However, it's worth noting that quantum speedup does not apply to all problems. Some problems are solved just as efficiently classically as they are quantum mechanically, and for others, we have yet to discover efficient quantum algorithms.

The key differentiators between classical and quantum algorithms lie in their operational principles and the laws of physics they are built upon. Quantum algorithms bring a novel approach to computation that has the potential to solve specific complex problems more efficiently.

*The Differences Between Classical Deterministic Algorithms and Quantum Probabilistic Algorithms*

Classical deterministic algorithms and quantum probabilistic algorithms operate under contrasting computational models, exemplifying the fundamental divide between classical and quantum computing. Both of these algorithmic constructs wield significant influence on the kind of problems they solve and how skillfully they do it.

In classical computing, deterministic algorithms underpin the operations. As the term 'deterministic' suggests, these algorithms follow a definite path of execution, producing a predictable and specific output for a given input. For instance, if we have a sorting algorithm like QuickSort or MergeSort, given an unsorted list as input, we know the algorithm will yield a sorted list as output. There is no randomness or probability involved in this process. Every time we run the algorithm with the same input, the intermediate steps and the output will always be the same. This determinism reflects the linear, ordered nature of classical computing processes, where each operation's outcome is certain.

In contrast, quantum computing introduces probabilistic algorithms due to its inherent probabilistic nature. Quantum mechanics' principles, which are inherently statistical, specify that we can only predict probabilities of outcomes, not the outcomes themselves. The superposition principle allows a qubit to exist simultaneously in multiple states, each with a certain probability amplitude. When a measurement is made, the qubit 'collapses' to one of these states based on the corresponding probability amplitudes.

Consider a quantum algorithm implemented on a quantum computer. Suppose we have a qubit in a superposition of states. When we measure this qubit, we obtain either '0' or '1', but we cannot predict which one with absolute certainty. The result of the measurement is naturally probabilistic, which means if we run the same quantum algorithm multiple times, we could get different results each time due to the random nature of quantum measurement. This probabilistic trait is fundamental to quantum algorithms.

How does this probabilistic nature matter? It's a double-edged sword. On one side, it's a source of quantum computing's power and potential speedup. Algorithms such as Grover's search algorithm exploit this quantum probability to search unsorted databases much faster than any classical algorithm. The probability amplitudes guide the algorithm, increasing the chances of finding the correct answer and decreasing the probabilities associated with incorrect ones.

On the flip side, the probabilistic outcomes of quantum algorithms present a challenge. Because we cannot determine the exact output of a quantum computation until we make a measurement, and this measurement can yield different results each time, we often have to run quantum algorithms multiple times to gain statistical confidence in the result. In addition, while quantum algorithms can provide superior performance for certain tasks, they require complex error correction techniques to manage quantum noise, a problem not encountered in classical deterministic algorithms.

In summary, the shift from classical deterministic algorithms to quantum probabilistic ones offers a new paradigm for computational problem-solving. This shift, however, is accompanied by unfamiliar challenges requiring sophisticated solutions. The probabilistic nature of quantum algorithms, entwined with quantum mechanical principles, facilitates a new landscape of computational possibilities and complexities. This intersection of certainty and probability makes quantum computing fascinating.

## Algorithms Can Provide Exponential Speedup

The potential of quantum algorithms to exponentially speed up solutions for specific computational tasks is like the sudden illumination of a dark, winding tunnel with a high-powered flashlight. The profound implications of this can be understood when we explore two quantum algorithms that have made a mark in the Quantum Cryptographic Cave: Shor's and Grover's algorithms.

*Shor's Algorithm*

Imagine standing in front of a gargantuan vault in our cryptographic cave, the lock of which consists of a large combined number, and you're tasked with finding its prime factors to unlock it. This scenario is parallel to RSA encryption, which relies on the difficulty of factoring large numbers as its security process. Classical computers, equipped with the best-known factoring algorithm, the General Number Field Sieve, could take ages to solve this. It's like trying to illuminate the vault with a dim candle, slowly and tediously examining each possible factor combination.

In stark contrast, Shor's algorithm, like a high-powered flashlight, cuts through the problem with efficiency. It leverages the unique power of quantum Fourier transform (QFT), which extracts the pattern of a specific function related to the factors of the number. This algorithm cleverly rewrites the factoring problem as a period finding problem, enabling us to utilize quantum parallelism and superposition to test multiple possibilities simultaneously. As such, it can potentially factorize large numbers in polynomial time - exponentially faster than the classical approach.

For instance, cracking a 2048-bit RSA encryption - a typical encryption level - with classical computers using brute force would, by some estimates, take longer than the age of the universe. However, with Shor's algorithm implemented on a fault-tolerant quantum computer, it could theoretically be done in a matter of days.

*Grover's Algorithm*

Next, imagine you are exploring a large unsorted database, which is like a vast, dark chamber filled with boxes. You're looking for a specific box - the proverbial needle in a haystack scenario. A classical search algorithm would require you to open and check each box one by one - a linear search - and in the worst-case scenario, you would need to check all boxes, which would be an $O(N)$ operation.

Enter Grover's algorithm, our quantum flashlight in this dark chamber. Instead of a linear search, Grover's algorithm leverages the principles of superposition and interference to search the unsorted 'database' quadratically faster in $O(\sqrt{N})$ operations. In this case, each operation is similar to 'opening a box' to see if it contains the item you're looking for.

To visualize this, imagine being able to 'open' multiple boxes simultaneously (thanks to quantum parallelism), and with each subsequent 'opening', you are more likely to find what you're looking for (thanks to quantum interference). For example, if you were searching through a database of one million entries, a classical algorithm might have to check each entry one by one, potentially making a million checks in the worst case. But with Grover's algorithm, you would only need to make about a thousand checks.

By shining a bright quantum light on the unique characteristics of Shor's and Grover's algorithms, we can understand how quantum algorithms can provide exponential speedups for certain computational tasks, leading to profound implications in cryptography and optimization fields.

## Exploring Notable Quantum Algorithms

The treasure hunt through our Cryptographic Caves of Quantum Computing now takes us deeper, towards the chambers of significant quantum algorithms. As we explore these chambers, let's unravel three key algorithms, namely, the Deutsch-Jozsa, the Bernstein-Vazirani, and Simon's algorithms. Each algorithm is a unique gem in the cave, displaying intriguing characteristics and showcasing the true capabilities of quantum computing.

*The Deutsch-Jozsa Algorithm*

This algorithm is among the earliest illustrations of quantum speedup. It's a problem-solving method designed to work on a quantum computer and demonstrate how quantum systems outperform our current computers. The Deutsch-Jozsa algorithm solves a particular type of problem known as the "oracle" problem exponentially faster than classical computers.

In an oracle problem, you're given a black box function that is either constant (always outputs the same value) or balanced (it outputs 0 for half of the input space and 1 for the other half). The task is to determine which type the function is. In the worst-case scenario, a classical computer would require up to 'n+1' queries to solve this, where 'n' is the number of inputs. However, the Deutsch-Jozsa algorithm can solve the same problem in just one query, showcasing an exponential speedup.

*The Bernstein-Vazirani Algorithm*

Moving further, we stumble upon another stunning gem, the Bernstein-Vazirani algorithm. This algorithm tackles a similar black-box problem as the Deutsch-Jozsa algorithm, but with a slight twist. The box holds a secret number, and the goal is to determine what that number is. The Bernstein-Vazirani algorithm again shows an exponential speedup over classical computers, solving the problem in just one query compared to 'n' queries required for a classical computer.

*Simon's Problem*

As we navigate further, we encounter Simon's Problem. This problem is about finding a hidden bit string that satisfies a specific property. While a classical algorithm would need to call the function a polynomial number of times, Simon's algorithm does it in linear time, highlighting yet another instance where quantum algorithms drastically outperform their classical counterparts.

These algorithms act as powerful guides demonstrating the trailblazing capabilities of quantum computing. Each algorithm, an embodiment of the power of quantum parallelism, offers unique insights into how quantum computers hold the potential to solve problems at a pace unimaginable for classical computers.

Illustrating that the key to unlocking the enormous computational potential of quantum computing lies in the clever design of quantum algorithms. The magic spells that, when cast upon the world of qubits, bring forth results in ways that can feel like nothing short of miraculous when viewed from the classical computing paradigm.

As we dive deeper into the Cryptographic Caves in the next sections, we'll uncover more about the design and workings of these significant quantum algorithms, thereby getting a closer view of the tantalizing treasures that quantum computing offers.

## Shor's Algorithm

*Integer factorization and its impact on cryptography*

Let's proceed deeper into the Cryptographic Caves and explore one of the most intriguing algorithms in quantum computing—Shor's algorithm, a marvel discovered by Peter Shor in 1994. The significance of Shor's algorithm lies in its capability to factorize large blended numbers into primes, an ability that could revolutionize the world of cryptography.

Shor's algorithm takes advantage of the characteristic properties of quantum computing, such as quantum parallelism and entanglement. This algorithm employs a classical reduction part and a quantum subroutine that uses modular exponentiation, demonstrating the intriguing teamwork of classical and quantum components within a quantum algorithm.

Understanding the inner workings of Shor's algorithm requires a glimpse into the principles of modular arithmetic, Quantum Fourier Transform (QFT), and period finding. The algorithm starts by randomly choosing a number, say 'a', less than the composite number 'N' we want to factor. If 'a' happens to share a factor with 'N', we've struck gold early. If not, the algorithm enters its quantum phase.

The quantum part of the algorithm deals with finding the period 'r' of the function f(x) = a^x mod N. Here, 'a' is the number we chose, and 'x' varies over integers. The function has a repeating pattern with some period 'r'.

The brilliance of Shor's algorithm lies in how it leverages quantum computing's ability to find this period 'r' efficiently. The function is loaded into a quantum register in superposition. A quantum Fourier transform is then applied to this register, enabling us to obtain information about the period 'r'. It's crucial to note that the Quantum Fourier Transform is a critical tool that enables the quantum phase estimation needed for finding the order 'r'. This is where the algorithm's bottleneck is - quantum modular exponentiation.

Once the period is found, it is used to identify the factors of 'N'. If 'r' is even and a^r/2 is not equivalent to -1 (mod N), then, gcd(a^r/2 ± 1, N) will give a non-trivial factor of 'N'.

The computational advantage of Shor's algorithm lies in the speedup it offers to the general number field sieve. It demonstrates an exponential advancement, making it vastly superior when dealing with large numbers. However, it's crucial to note that implementing Shor's algorithm requires large-scale quantum computers, which, as of now, are beyond existing technology.

The practical implications of Shor's algorithm are profound, particularly for cryptography. Traditional encryption methods, including RSA, rely on the hardness of factorizing large prime numbers. Shor's algorithm, with its ability to factorize large numbers efficiently, could potentially break these encryption codes, necessitating a seismic shift in our current cryptographic systems.

Shor's algorithm is a testament to the revolutionary potential of quantum computing. Its ability could potentially change the landscape of cryptography and computer security. As our quantum capabilities continue to grow, it becomes increasingly essential to understand such algorithms and prepare for their eventual implementation.

## Exploration of Grover's algorithm

Let's advance into Grover's Algorithm, an ingenious creation in the quantum computing world. Introduced by Lov Grover in 1996, this algorithm illuminates the potential of quantum computers to solve search and optimization problems with a level of productivity that classical computers can't match.

At the heart of Grover's algorithm is the ability to search a disorderly database. Picture a haystack with a needle buried somewhere within. A classical computer would have to check each strand of hay, one by one until it finds the needle. However, Grover's algorithm, equipped with the power of quantum superposition, interference, and amplitude amplification, will achieve this assignment significantly faster.

The algorithm begins with a quantum state that is an equal superposition of all possible solutions. It then applies a sequence of operations (known as Grover's iteration) that incrementally amplify the amplitude of the correct answer while diminishing that of incorrect ones. As a result, when a measurement is made, the quantum state collapses to the correct answer with a high probability. This is a quantum analog of 'peeking' into each box all at once, but in a way that fundamentally respects the rules of quantum physics.

However, it's not just about finding a single needle in a haystack. Grover's algorithm also has broader applications in optimization problems, which are everywhere in our world. Everything from machine learning and cryptography to Explainable AI and wireless channel assignment can benefit from the power of this quantum algorithm.

Consider the problem of finding the minimum (or maximum) of a function - a fundamental task in optimization. By translating this task into a search problem, Grover's algorithm can be used to find the optimal solution. For instance, in machine learning, we often seek the model parameters that minimize the loss function, which could be cast as a search problem over the parameter space.

But, as with all algorithms, Grover's is not without its limitations. The need for a quantum oracle - a black box operation used to encode the problem into a quantum computer - can be a practical hurdle. Furthermore, the complexity of the algorithm scales exponentially with the number of qubits, which can be challenging given current quantum hardware.

However, even with these challenges, the significance of Grover's algorithm in the quantum computing landscape cannot be understated. It showcases the power of quantum computation to offer speedups over classical methods, opening the door to tackling complex problems in new and efficient ways.

As our understanding and development of quantum computing continues to grow, so will our appreciation for the power and potential of algorithms like Grover's. They provide a glimpse into what is possible with quantum computers and inspire new ways of thinking about computational problems. It's indeed an exciting time to be part of the quantum rising.

## Introduction to the Quantum Fourier Transform (QFT)

Venture with us now into the Quantum Fourier Transform (QFT), an indispensable tool in quantum algorithms, a jewel in the crown of quantum computation. Like its classical counterpart, the Fourier transform, the QFT is a method for revealing the frequency components of a signal, but with the unique quantum ability to operate on quantum states in superposition.

Just as the classical Fourier transform allows us to decompose a signal into its core frequencies, the QFT lets us dissect a quantum state into its inherent quantum frequencies. Yet, it's not a mere translation of the classical method into the quantum world; it's a fundamentally new tool, intricately woven with the fabric of quantum mechanics. The QFT exhibits its quantum nature by effectively dealing with states in superposition.

One of the most striking applications of the QFT is in Shor's algorithm for factorization. In essence, Shor's algorithm cleverly transforms the factoring problem into a period-finding problem. Once the period is found, factorization becomes a breeze. But how does one find the period of a quantum state? Enter the QFT. Shor's algorithm applies the QFT to a superposition of states encoding different multiples of the period, which causes the various frequency components to interfere constructively at the correct answer while canceling each other out elsewhere. When a measurement is made, the quantum state collapses to an answer with a high probability. The likely result is a dramatic speedup over classical factorization algorithms.

Additionally, the QFT plays a central role in quantum phase estimation, a critical subroutine in many quantum algorithms, and can be instrumental in tasks such as eigenvalue estimation and quantum search. Despite its extraordinary potential, it is important to note that challenges in preparing and measuring quantum states currently limit the QFT's applications. Moreover, not all aspects of

QFT-based computation offer exponential speedup, and resource requirements, especially memory, are significant in many-body models.

The beauty of the Quantum Fourier Transform is not just in its mathematical elegance but also in its practical implications for the future of computation. But to truly appreciate and use it, one needs to build quantum intuition and skills. Engaging with interactive tools, visualization techniques, and practice exercises can aid this learning process.

The Quantum Fourier Transform stands as a beacon, illuminating the extreme potential of quantum computing and reminding us of the challenges that lie ahead. As we continue our journey into the quantum domain, the QFT will undoubtedly remain a trusted companion and a guiding light.

## (QAOA) Explore the Quantum Approximate Optimization Algorithm

The Quantum Approximate Optimization Algorithm, often referred to by its acronym QAOA, is one of the most promising developments in quantum computing. This algorithm is devised to solve a wide range of optimization problems more efficiently than traditional methods. It leverages the principles of quantum mechanics to traverse the solution space in ways that classical computers can't.

To appreciate the power of QAOA, it's helpful to think of optimization problems as trying to find the lowest point in a landscape of hills and valleys. This landscape can represent anything from logistical challenges, like finding the most efficient route for delivery trucks, to financial quandaries, like portfolio optimization in finance.

A classical algorithm would typically 'walk' across this landscape, trying different routes and continuously adjusting its path based on the 'altitude' it finds. The more complex the landscape, the more likely the classical algorithm might get stuck in a 'local minimum' – a valley that isn't the lowest point but appears to be from the immediate perspective.

On the other hand, QAOA acts like a skilled bird soaring above the landscape, able to assess the terrain from a much broader perspective. It utilizes quantum superposition to 'be' in multiple places at once and quantum interference to navigate the solution space more efficiently, making it less likely to get trapped in local minimums.

See the "Traveling Salesman Problem" (TSP), a famous optimization challenge. The problem involves a salesman who needs to visit several cities once and return to the origin city while minimizing the total travel distance. For a handful of cities, solving this isn't too hard. But as you add more cities, the number of possible routes grows astronomically.

When a classical computer solves the TSP, it might start with one path, assess its length, then try another and another. Even with some clever shortcuts, the classical algorithm could still take an impractically long time if we have many cities.

By contrast, a quantum computer running QAOA could consider multiple routes simultaneously thanks to quantum superposition, and then use quantum interference to guide the system toward the shortest route. While we might not be able to run QAOA efficiently for large TSPs on existing quantum computers due to their limited size and noise issues, the algorithm represents a tantalizing glimpse of what could be possible as quantum technology advances.

Like all quantum algorithms, it's important to note that QAOA isn't a magic bullet that will solve all problems better than classical methods. But for a particular class of complex optimization problems, it promises substantial efficiency gains and points the way to the sorts of tasks future quantum computers might excel at.

To harness the full power of QAOA, though, we need to continue refining quantum hardware and developing effective quantum software. That's an ongoing project involving physicists, computer scientists, and mathematicians across the globe, a collaborative effort that will, we hope, lead us into the next era of computing.

## QPE

Quantum Phase Estimation (QPE) is a fundamental tool in the quantum computing toolbox. At its heart, QPE is about precision - specifically, the precise estimation of eigenvalues, which are critical values associated with mathematical objects called operators.

To understand QPE, imagine you're a musician tuning an instrument. Each string on the instrument can play a variety of tones, but there's one fundamental tone, or eigenvalue, which corresponds to the main vibration frequency of the string. It's a bit like this with QPE: you're 'tuning' your quantum system to find the eigenvalue of an operator, which gives you valuable information about the system's behavior.

But how does this 'tuning' work in practice? QPE exploits the unique features of quantum mechanics - interference and superposition - to estimate the phase (another name for the angle in wave mechanics) of an eigenstate of a unitary operator.

To illustrate this, let's revisit our musician example. Suppose each note of the instrument is an eigenstate, and the sound produced is the phase. Our musician plays all notes (superposition), listens to the resulting sound (interference), and then identifies the loudest (dominant) note. This process is similar to the QPE process of phase estimation.

The power lies in its precision and efficiency. It can pick out the key 'notes' from a quantum 'chord symbol', enabling us to understand and harness our quantum systems' behaviors more effectively. This 'tuning' process is why QPE is fundamental to various quantum algorithms.

QPE is not just about theoretical beauty; it has practical applications, too. It plays a critical role in Shor's factoring algorithm, enabling the efficient factorization of large numbers, with implications for cryptography. Additionally, QPE forms the basis for quantum algorithms designed to simulate physical systems, where understanding the eigenvalues of certain operators can provide insight into the system's properties.

Quantum Phase Estimation is like the 'tuning' process for quantum algorithms. It pinpoints the key frequencies that allow quantum systems to 'sing' in harmony with computational tasks, making it a cornerstone of many quantum algorithm designs.

## Solving Linear Algorithms

*Description of the HHL Algorithm*

Imagine yourself as a spelunker descending deeper into the cryptographic cave. Suddenly, you encounter an intricate network of interconnected caves, each leading to a different treasure. These paths and their interconnectedness can be represented as a system of linear equations, where each path represents a variable, and their intersections represent the relationships between the variables. Here, the Harrow-Hassidim-Lloyd (HHL) algorithm serves as our guide through this labyrinth, helping us determine the most efficient path to the treasures.

The HHL algorithm employs three primary steps:

1. **State Preparation**: This phase represents the initial mapping of our cave system. The algorithm creates a quantum state that corresponds to the right-hand side of our linear system, serving as the starting point of our exploration.

2. **Quantum Phase Estimation**: This step involves identifying key features of the cave system (eigenvalues) that can help us plan our exploration most efficiently. It's like estimating different cave paths' lengths, difficulties, and intersections.

3. **Conditional Rotation and Uncomputation**: Here, we fine-tune our exploration plan based on the identified cave features. The state of an auxiliary qubit is rotated inversely proportional to the features identified. Following that, we reverse the Quantum Phase Estimation operation to get our final route plan.

## Example Implementation of the HHL Algorithm

Let's use a financial example to demonstrate the algorithm's power. Suppose we're trying to optimize a stock portfolio where each stock's future price depends on various economic factors. These relationships can be represented as a system of linear equations, with each stock being a path in our cave system and the intersections representing the dependencies between different stocks.

With the HHL algorithm, we can prepare our initial portfolio (State Preparation), identify key financial trends and dependencies (Quantum Phase Estimation), and adjust our portfolio accordingly to maximize profits while minimizing risks (Conditional Rotation and Uncomputation).

By unlocking the treasure chest of optimized stock portfolios, the HHL algorithm not only demonstrates its prowess in solving complex linear systems but also illustrates the far-reaching impacts of quantum computation in fields as diverse as finance, logistics, AI, and beyond.

## Applications of Quantum Algorithms in Various Fields

With their unconventional computation methods, Quantum algorithms promise transformative shifts across a wide range of sectors. Let's dive into these vibrant seas, exploring various islands where quantum computation finds its applications.

1. **Healthcare and Drug Discovery**: A significant treasure in our cryptographic cave is drug discovery. Pharmaceutical companies often sift through a vast database of molecular structures in search of potential drug candidates. Quantum algorithms, especially Grover's, could perform this task exponentially faster than classical algorithms, speeding up the discovery process. This could revolutionize how we fight diseases, enabling personalized medicine and rapid response to pandemics.

2. **Financial Services**: Financial institutions handle massive amounts of complex and computationally intensive tasks such as risk analysis, portfolio optimization, and pricing derivatives. Algorithms like the Quantum Approximate Optimization Algorithm (QAOA) could provide solutions to these complex problems much faster and more accurately than their classical counterparts, potentially saving billions of dollars.

3. **Logistics and Supply Chain**: The vast network of global supply chains, filled with countless routes, can be optimized using quantum algorithms. The HHL algorithm, for example, can solve linear systems and optimize routes, reducing costs and increasing efficiency.

4. **Energy and Climate Science**: Quantum algorithms could be game-changers in the modeling and analysis of environmental systems. Accurate simulations of molecular interactions and climate

models could help design more efficient renewable energy sources and predict climate changes with high precision.

5. **Material Science**: Quantum computing could revolutionize material science by enabling the simulation of quantum systems. Quantum Phase Estimation, used to precisely estimate eigenvalues, could help discover new materials with desired properties, opening doors to innovations in various fields from electronics to aerospace.

As we leave our cryptographic cave of quantum algorithms, we bring with us a trove of treasures ready to solve some of the most complex problems across various fields. As we venture further into the domain of quantum computing in the following chapters, it's crucial to remember that while quantum computing is powerful, it is a tool. Like any tool, its power lies in how we use it.

It is an exciting time in the field of quantum computing. As we stand on the edge of this technological revolution, we are on the cusp of uncovering an entirely new landscape of computational possibilities. As quantum algorithms continue to evolve, they will undeniably shape our future, from medicine to finance, supply chains to climate science, and beyond. Quantum computing is not just a new technology but a new way of approaching the world.

Thus, we wrap up our journey into the fascinating world of quantum algorithms in this chapter. However, this is not an ending but rather a launchpad, propelling us deeper into the quantum universe. Exploring more quantum wonders and their potential impacts.

# Chapter 5

## Practical Applications of Quantum Tech

### Where Theory Meets Practice

In quantum computing, the line between theory and application often seems blurred—a fantastical landscape where math and metaphysics merge, opening up avenues for change that were once considered the stuff of science fiction. As we've journeyed through the foundational elements and tackled common misconceptions, it's now time to delve into the core of where quantum technology meets real-world applications.

You're about to step into a promising oasis of innovation—a quantum city, if you will. This bustling hub holds the map of transformative quantum uses, similar to the foundational elements of a thriving community. Imagine healthcare, finance, logistics, and cybersecurity, all improved by the power of qubits and superposition, and every challenge is met with pioneering solutions, courtesy of quantum algorithms.

But every city has its struggles, and our quantum utopia is no exception. Alongside its awe-inspiring skyscrapers of potential, there are roadblocks, bottlenecks, and unfulfilled promises. You'll learn about the existing limitations of quantum technology, ensuring you gain a balanced perspective on this groundbreaking field. Your active participation will deepen your understanding and demonstrate how quantum can reshape decision-making and transform workflows.

As we explore the expansive landscape of quantum computing applications, we'll also turn our eyes toward the horizon. The rapidly evolving nature of this field means that today's limitations could be tomorrow's breakthroughs. We'll examine what experts predict for the coming decade, presenting you with a future outlook that's as scientifically grounded as it is awe-inspiringly vast.

Intrigued? We thought you might be. Stick with us to the end for a special opportunity to take your quantum computing journey even further.

Let's dive in.

## Existing and Potential Applications of Quantum Computing

Welcome to The City, crowded with possibilities and promise, where the marriage of quantum mechanics and computational power is breathing new life into multiple industries. From healthcare to finance, logistics to cybersecurity, and even in sectors we're just beginning to understand, quantum computing is shaping up as a transformational force that will redefine our familiarity with the world around us.

As Nobel winner Richard Feynman once said, "What I cannot create, I do not understand." And in this ambitious effort to create a new standard of computing, we're also taking leaps in understanding the complexities of our universe, one qubit at a time, ushering in a new era of computational ability.

But what are the tangible, successful applications where quantum computing excels in our approach? In the coming pages, we will get into the nitty-gritty of quantum computing applications in drug discovery, materials science, healthcare, finance, and even marketing. Moreover, we'll touch on the synergistic relationship between quantum computing and Artificial Intelligence, particularly in natural language processing.

I hope to equip you with the knowledge needed to appreciate the profound impact that quantum computing could have on society at large. It's time to explore the growing infrastructure already taking shape at the intersections of industry, science, and technology.

## The Quantum Advantage in Accelerating Breakthroughs

"Quantum computing could be game-changing for drug development in the pharmaceutical industry. Businesses should start preparing now." - Expert analysis from McKinsey & Company.

Imagine a world where the creation of new drugs doesn't take decades of research and billions of dollars, but instead is dramatically accelerated, saving countless lives and resources. Welcome to the crossroads where quantum computing collides with drug discovery and molecular simulations, unlocking pathways to treatments once thought to be years away from realization.

## An In-depth Exploration

Channeling the spirit of Richard Feynman's assertion that to simulate nature, one must think quantum, this merging of quantum mechanics with molecular science has become pivotal in refining our knowledge of molecular behaviors and interactions. We are no longer confined to yesterday's approximations; today's quantum-infused drug discovery field is both optimized and expansive.

Molecular simulations are now at the vanguard, elucidating the complex dance of biomolecules and their interplay with prospective drug entities. Such modeling, vital to drug discovery, equips researchers with predictive tools, revealing how potential drugs interact within biological systems. For instance, molecular modeling played a role in devising inhibitors targeting enzymes or receptors. Visualizing a drug molecule's snug fit within a target's active site fast-tracks the drug design trajectory.

Further enhancing our understanding are Molecular Dynamics (MD) simulations, which provide a cinematic view of molecular interactions unfolding over time. Such insights were instrumental in grasping the dynamic nature of the HIV-1 protease enzyme, paving the way for inhibitors that have since become pillars of antiretroviral treatments.

Introducing artificial intelligence (AI) to this mix signals a transformative juncture. With its predictive skills, AI streamlines the drug discovery journey, hinting at molecules with therapeutic potential, refining them for optimal efficacy, and even forecasting potential side effects. A testament to AI's clout lies in its instrumental role during health emergencies, swiftly repurposing existing drugs for newfound uses.

Merging these theoretical frameworks with hands-on lab experiments is already productive in drug research. "Real World Drug Discovery: A Chemist's Guide to Biotech and Pharmaceutical Research by Robert M. Rydzewski" describes numerous instances where theory and practice harmoniously united, giving birth to potent therapeutics.

Quantum computing is bridging crucial gaps. The World Health Organization underscores the essence of innovation in widening access to medicines. With computational techniques and molecular simulations slashing traditional drug discovery timelines and expenses, we can refocus on previously overlooked diseases and render novel medications.

For those inclined towards visual aids, many online platforms explain molecular dynamics simulations in drug discovery. One commendable video, "Application of molecular dynamics simulations in drug discovery by BioExcel CoE," offers an engaging dive into the potential and processes that molecular dynamics simulations promise.

However, it's crucial to temper optimism with sensibility. As the field expands, challenges loom, especially in talent cultivation, an issue discussed in the next chapter. A balanced strategy accounting for potential impediments will be mandatory as the pharmaceutical industry gears up to exploit the quantum edge.

Yet, the quantum journey extends beyond drug discovery. The healthcare sector, especially personalized medicine, stands to reap quantum benefits. As we continue, we'll unearth how quantum performance promises to reshape healthcare, championing diagnostics and tailor-made treatments that are effective and safer for patients.

## The Quantum Edge in Personalized Medicine

*"Quantum technologies are set to transform healthcare, making diagnostics more precise and treatments more individualized than ever."*

- Harvard Medical School.

Imagine a future, not so distant, where each medical intervention is tailored to your unique genetic makeup, health history, and specific needs. Such personalization is becoming a reality, thanks to the union of quantum computing and medical science.

Richard Feynman, a pioneer in quantum mechanics, observed the inherent quantum nature of biological systems. Today, that very connection between quantum mechanics and biology is transforming our approach to medicine. The age-old 'one-size-fits-all' treatment method is shifting to a nuanced, quantum-informed strategy. A prime example of this transformation lies in genetic sequencing. With the promise of quantum capabilities, what was once a monumental challenge in decoding the human genome can now be faster and remarkably precise. This rapid sequencing doesn't just enhance our understanding of genetic ailments; it empowers physicians to recommend treatments aligning perfectly with an individual's genetic code.

Diagnostics are on the cusp of a quantum leap. Advanced imaging techniques, like MRI, stand to benefit greatly from quantum-enhanced sensors. With superior resolution and speed, these sensors promise earlier and incredibly accurate disease detection. But the quantum revolution doesn't stop there. Pairing quantum computing with artificial intelligence is generating algorithms capable of sifting through vast medical datasets in mere moments. With their outstanding analytical expertise, such algorithms unveiled patterns that were previously invisible, offering breakthroughs like predicting cardiac events with startling accuracy.

For those seeking tangible examples, "Artificial Intelligence in Healthcare: Unlocking Its Potential by Dr. Janak Gunatilleke" serves as a beacon, detailing various instances where quantum methodologies are already reshaping medical landscapes. Be it swift drug trials or cutting-edge brain imaging techniques, the transformative potential of quantum in healthcare seems limitless.

Of course, like all seismic shifts, the quantum pivot in healthcare brings its own set of concerns, from patient privacy to key ethical considerations. Addressing these will be critical as we forge ahead, ensuring that our quantum healthcare journey is groundbreaking and responsible.

As we continue, it becomes evident that the potential applications of quantum computing influence a spectrum of industries. From reshaping logistical networks to pioneering intelligent energy solutions, the ripple effect of quantum computing is profound and far-reaching. Let's see its impact on materials science and engineering.

## The Quantum Revolution in Advanced Materials

*"Quantum mechanics promises a future where material properties are not just discovered but designed."*

- MIT Department of Materials Science and Engineering.

Picture a world where everyday items possess material attributes fine-tuned to our precise demands. A future where we don't merely stumble upon material properties, but meticulously craft them using quantum mechanics. Think metals, ceramics, and polymers, all sculpted atom-by-atom to peak performance. It's no daydream; quantum computing is birthing this new era of material mastery.

At the core of this formation lies the intimate bond between quantum mechanics and materials. Scientists have long recognized the quantum dance of materials at minuscule atomic scales. Now, with quantum computing, we can leverage this knowledge, giving birth to materials boasting unheard-of properties, primed to tackle today's most pressing obstacles.

Consider the quest for room-temperature superconductors, a materials science dream. Quantum computing's skill in simulating complex electron bonds edges us closer to this goal, anticipating the dawn of power-efficient grids and cutting-edge transport mechanisms.

In this quantum-augmented world, polymers can be intricately tailored to exhibit desired mechanical, thermal, or electrical characteristics. Nanoparticles are also fine-tuned for industries ranging from precise drug delivery to advancing solar tech and pioneering electronics. The results are breathtaking when we marry AI's predictive powers with quantum computing. This union predicts material behaviors with remarkable precision, fast-tracking discoveries that once spanned generations into mere moments.

To go deeper, get the book, "Artificial Intelligence for Materials Science by Yuan Cheng, Tian Wang, and Gang Zhang," which offers a treasure trove of cases. It has a searchable and interactive database where quantum computing has reshaped the fabric of material research, be it in birthing corrosion-defiant alloys or sculpting bio-compatible marvels for medical implants.

Reflecting on the UN's clear call for sustainable industrial evolution, the quantum materials research movement has a pivotal role. It's not just about crafting cutting-edge materials but designing eco-conscious materials and efficient recycling methodologies to conserve our beautiful planet.

Those with an appetite for visual narratives can turn to platforms like YouTube. The video "The Strange New Universe of Quantum Materials - Piers Coleman Rutgers University" paints a vivid scene of quantum computing's ability with material innovation.

Yet, as with any process, there are hurdles. As we analyze and create quantum materials, issues ranging from intellectual property to regulatory intricacies and ethical considerations (especially as materials begin to meld with biology) demand our attention. These topics and more will be explored in the final chapter.

While life sciences are reaping quantum dividends, it's just the tip of the iceberg. Next, we will navigate the quantum-driven boost in

Finance and portfolio management, unraveling a future that once seemed confined to a handful of analytical categories.

## A Quantum Leap in Financial Forecasting

In the honorable corridors of the Wharton School of Finance, a prediction echoes: Quantum algorithms are set to transform the field of financial strategies, evolving portfolio optimization into an art of uncharted precision. Such accuracy promises a future where economic decisions aren't merely anchored in past experiences, but are informed by the profound foresight offered by quantum-predicted market movements. The dream of avoiding pitfalls with your best educated guess gradually fades away as quantum computations take the spotlight. Indeed, the world of finance is on the cusp of a quantum alignment.

The challenge of predicting the unpredictable, ever-fluctuating market scenarios, has been finance's on-going quest. Traditional computing has made honorable feats, yet it has its limitations when navigating the complex maze of financial variables. Here's where quantum computing advertises its entry, poised to reshape financial forecasting with capabilities that were once elusive.

Portfolio management has always been a delicate balance—seizing lucrative opportunities on the one hand and skirting risks on the other. We can design a system that simulates thousands of market scenarios through quantum algorithms, painting a holistic, multi-faceted view of the potential rewards and threats.

Currency exchange, with its rapid fluctuations, presents its own set of challenges. Even the slightest predictive advantage can yield transformative results in this volatile market. Quantum algorithms offer the edge that can make all the difference; even if it's the tiniest of margins, they could easily outpace traditional systems.

A new alliance is emerging on the horizon—the powerful merger of AI's pattern recognition paired with quantum computing's unmatched speed. As these two titans unite, they promise to revolutionize algorithmic trading, sifting through vast reservoirs of trade data, global news, and key event signals to anticipate market movements like never before.

Diving into the real-world manifestations of this quantum trajectory, the book "Quantum Machine Learning and Optimisation in Finance by Antoine Jacquier and Oleksiy Kondratyev" shines a light on the groundbreaking applications of quantum principles in the financial sector. From ensuring airtight security through quantum-encrypted transactions to pioneering hedge fund strategies, the financial field is undergoing a transformative shift right before our eyes.

The potential of quantum computing extends beyond simple innovation. Its promise of sharpened financial services and predictions also invites a future of reduced transaction costs. For those with an inclination towards visual learning, resources abound. Platforms like YouTube offer a window into this evolving world, with content like "Quantum Computing for Finance by Centre for Quantum Technologies" showing an in-depth look into how quantum principles redefine the financial sphere.

The financial sector must remain vigilant as challenges arise. Concerns ranging from the ethical implications of ultra-fast quantum trades to the sanctity of data in the era of quantum cryptography need careful deliberation. As financial institutions brace themselves for this quantum leap, they must be equipped with more than just shiny new technology—a calibrated moral compass will be equally essential.

The narrative of quantum computing and its transformative potential is vast and varied. We've only scratched the surface and must explore its implications for marketing and optimization; let's continue.

## The Quantum Future of Marketing Strategy

*"Quantum computing could revolutionize the world of marketing, personalizing user experiences to an unprecedented degree."*

- Harvard Business Review.

Harvard Business Review foresees a future where marketing messages aren't generic but tailored with a quantum precision that feels almost intuitive. Quantum computing will enhance marketing with supernatural awareness. Imagine stepping into a world where the line between a customer's wants and a brand's offering is always aligned. That isn't a fantasy; it's the emerging reality where quantum computing and marketing optimization beautifully intersect.

In the digital age we inhabit, every interaction, from a simple click to a share, is a piece of a larger puzzle, one that gives insights into user behavior and preferences. With its awe-inspiring capacity to swiftly navigate vast oceans of data, Quantum computing promises to evolve these interactions. For brands, every digital footprint could soon translate into an invaluable opportunity, crafting user profiles with a level of personalization that's unprecedented.

While traditional systems may ponder over which ads hit the mark, quantum algorithms cut to the chase. Their capacity allows them to evaluate a multitude of ad variations simultaneously, transforming the marketing landscape by fine-tuning campaigns in what feels like a heartbeat.

Central to any brand's strategy is understanding the consumer journey. This pathway can be intricate, riddled with choices, preferences, and emotions. However, quantum computing, armed with its ability to envision countless consumer paths in the blink of an eye, stands to empower businesses. Brands can potentially foresee and cater to a consumer's needs even before they come to the surface.

Now, let's picture quantum computing's merger with AI in marketing. The result? A transformative approach to predictive analytics. This synergy promises capabilities that stretch from pinpointing growing trends to revealing subtle patterns in consumer behaviors, thereby redefining marketing's predictive game.

The book "The Business Case for AI by Kavita Ganesan" delves deep into this evolving nexus of quantum technology and marketing strategies. It introduces the numerous ways in which pioneering brands harness quantum algorithms, refining their approach from customer details to the nuances of retargeting. By leveraging quantum insights, brands have the potential to craft campaigns that resonate across a spectrum of audiences and expand their reach.

However, as the marketing realm teeters on the brink of this quantum customization, it faces challenges from the sanctity of data sovereignty to the ethical navigation of hyper-personalized insights. Yet, the tale of quantum computing's influence isn't confined to marketing. It's time to explore one of my favorites, AI and Natural Language Processing, to discover how quantum advancements might sculpt our future.

## Harnessing the Quantum Realm for AI and NLP

*"It's not about the bits, it's about what you do with them."*

- John Maeda

Ah, Natural Language Processing (NLP). For those of you who might be working in tech, or at least keenly following its rapid innovations, you're likely familiar with NLP. In layman's terms, it's a technology that helps machines understand, interpret, and respond to human languages in a meaningful and contextually appropriate way. For a good stretch, we've been reliant on classical computing to perform these tasks. But let's turn our gaze to something even more cutting-edge. I'm talking about Quantum Natural Language Processing (QNLP), a new frontier that could redefine how we understand communication, language, and interaction in the digital space.

Imagine a reality where our machines transcend mere language understanding. Instead, they truly comprehend, discerning not only our words but the very emotions, subtleties, and contexts that accompany them. As the formidable forces of quantum computing and AI-powered NLP converge, we teeter on the cusp of an era marked by machines that intuitively interact with humans, responding with a supernatural grasp of context and emotion.

Where traditional deep learning models, so integral to NLP endeavors, often found themselves resource-strapped, quantum-enhanced models are rewriting the script. These quantum-infused algorithms ride a wave of efficiency in processing NLP tasks. Whether it's the intricate dance of machine translation or the delicate art of sentiment analysis, quantum mechanisms are poised to redefine their horizons.

In the expansive field of text analysis, quantum computing promises to be nothing short of transformative. Think of it as giving machines the ability to speed-read and comprehend libraries' worth of text in just moments, all while extracting context-rich insights that conventional systems might overlook. This quantum speed is set to recalibrate the very foundations of text analysis.

When AI, with its relentless data-driven hunger, melds with quantum computing's unmatched processing might, the results for NLP could be breathtaking. Models could evolve to exhibit heightened accuracy, embracing adaptability and an acute sense of context like never before.

Picture this real-world implication: Customer support chatbots that, instead of offering bland, generic responses, discern the sentiment that underscores a customer's words. Or voice assistants that remember and learn from past conversations, evolving to provide a seamless conversational experience. This isn't a distant future dream—it's the tangible potential of quantum-infused NLP.

As we grant our machines this heightened awareness and understanding, ethical considerations have become front and center, especially around data privacy. The idea of hyper-aware AI systems introduces questions and concerns that our chapter on ethics promises to discuss.

The marriage of quantum computing with NLP signifies more than a simple technological stride—it's a notable shift in our very dialogue with machines. And as we dig deep into this quantum world, we stand ready to uncover its transformative potential across industries and society.

## The Quantum Quandary in Cybersecurity

*"Quantum computing, with its dual capability, stands poised to redefine the future of secure communications while simultaneously challenging existing encryption protocols."*

- Harvard Business Review.

Visualize quantum computing in the domain of cybersecurity as a double-edged sword. Its gleaming edge promises a fortress of security, paving the way for methods like quantum key distribution, which can render covert eavesdropping ineffective. Yet, its other edge casts a shadow, hinting at the potential vulnerabilities it could introduce, potentially shattering many of our current cryptographic safeguards.

At the heart of this new era of secure communications is Quantum Key Distribution (QKD). This isn't sophisticated tech jargon. It's a critical change in our understanding and approach to encrypted communications. By harnessing the features of quantum mechanics, QKD sets a new gold standard in secure transmissions. While the quantum domain readies its suite of advanced encryption tools, there lies a pressing, inescapable quest to future-proof our classical cryptographic methods. As quantum computers edge closer to cracking these methods, the evolution towards post-quantum cryptography, impenetrable to quantum decryption attacks, becomes paramount.

The era of quantum in cybersecurity is dawning. As this technology becomes more intertwined with our systems, a dual mandate emerges for industries and governments alike. First, they must harness the positive quantum tidal wave ushering in credible, secure communications. Together, they must fortify their classical systems, guarding them against the potential quantum breaches looming on the horizon.

Chapter 7 offers a deep dive into this mesmerizing dance between quantum computing and cryptography, exploring its challenges and innovative solutions. But as we continue exploring the quantum domain, we're set to see how it's intertwining with other modern technological wonders.

## Grappling with the Subtleties of Quantum Computing's Challenges

*"Every frontier of innovation has its shadows, and in understanding them, we illuminate our path forward."*

- Commeum Frontiers Journal.

The rise of quantum computing, as transformative as it has been projected to be, is not without its challenges, intricate and multi-dimensional, beyond technology and hardware, affecting our world's economic, educational, and security fields.

Starting with the **knowledge and talent gap**, it's evident that quantum computing's complexity requires a unique blend of expertise. Bridging the worlds of quantum mechanics and computational applications demands professionals who are not only versed in the abstract intricacies of quantum theory but are also skilled at its practical application in real-world computational settings. The quantum depth chart of talent is currently sparse in the academic and professional landscapes. As universities and institutions work to develop curricula that nurture this blend of expertise, industries, too, face the challenge of attracting, training, and retaining this rare talent.

On the **economic front**, the quantum field presents a paradox. While its long-term potential is undoubtedly expansive, realizing this potential requires significant upfront investment, both in terms of capital and time. This presents a delicate balancing act for businesses and investors: weighing the promise of profound breakthroughs against substantial short-term financial commitments. Moreover, the commercialization of quantum technologies requires not just investment in hardware and research but also in public understanding, policy frameworks, and infrastructure.

Lastly, **security concerns** loom large. Quantum computing, with its potential to crack existing cryptographic methods, ushers in an era where our traditional concepts of data protection might be rendered obsolete. However, this very threat is also a beacon of innovation. It sparks the development of quantum-safe encryption methods and the exploration of inherently secure quantum communication techniques like quantum key distribution. Transitioning to these new security protocols while safeguarding our digital world is challenging, even with global collaboration and policy-making.

In wrapping our minds around these challenges, we're addressing the roadblocks and setting the stage for a solid and resilient quantum future. In the following chapters, readers will gain insights into the problems and the numerous solutions and strategies being developed globally to navigate them.

## Quantum Leap Forward

This chapter has unveiled the practical potential of quantum computing across various industries, highlighting its transformative promise. However, understanding is just the first step. It's an invitation for readers—students, professionals, and enthusiasts alike—to dive deeper, experiment, and innovate. As we transition to Chapter 6, we'll explore quantum computing's broader impact on technology and careers.

The future of quantum is not just in its computations but in its capacity to reshape our industries. Are you ready to embrace this quantum shift?

# CHAPTER 6

## MAPPING QUANTUM COMPUTING

### The Future of Tech and Careers

Quantum computing is reshaping the tech landscape faster than we think. And here's the exciting part: This isn't just about the distant future. It's about you, right now. Have you wondered how can I stand out in my career? Or how can my business jump ahead of the curve, leveraging the latest AI and quantum advancements?

In simple words, quantum computing is like the next big adventure in the world of technology. Think of it as a mountain. Every time you reach a new summit, you discover higher peaks. For some, it's about finding new job opportunities. For others, it's about growing their company and getting ahead of the competition.

Here's some promising news: Experts think AI and quantum computing will create 100 million new jobs. That's huge! Many companies have already started using this new tech, and guess what? They need people like you and me to help them out.

In this chapter, I'll be your guide, like the friend who shows you the best paths on a hike—pointing out the big changes quantum computing will bring. Even better, I'll show you where to learn skill development and get started today. We call this the "Quantum

Toolkit". It's like a backpack filled with everything you need for your climb: helpful websites, courses, and tips.

So, gear up to explore the impact on technology and your career. We're about to start a fantastic hike with quantum computing as our compass. Let's climb this mountain together and see all the cool things waiting for us at the top!

## How Quantum Changes Key Jobs and Businesses

*Quantum's Edge in Marketing*

At its core, marketing thrives on understanding and predicting consumer behavior. In our digital age, this translates to sifting through vast amounts of data to decode patterns and trends. Enter quantum computing! Unlike traditional systems that may stagger under the sheer volume of consumer data, quantum computers discern patterns in mere seconds, making trend predictions more accurate and efficient than ever before.

We've already glimpsed the transformative power of AI in marketing. Who hasn't been captivated by the viral Lensa AI app that creates 'magic avatars' from our photos, transporting us to the cosmos as astronauts or reincarnating us as famous figures from history? Now, envision this AI genius supercharged by quantum computing. The potential is staggering: campaigns that don't just analyze user data but preemptively gauge and adapt to consumer preferences, often before the consumers themselves even consciously realize them. In this dynamic landscape, marketers who blend quantum-driven analytics with innovative strategies will lead the charge.

In preparation, aspiring marketers shall not be discouraged by the complexity of quantum mechanics. There are resources designed specifically for the layperson, such as courses on Google's Quantum AI campus, that distill intricate concepts into digestible insights. With a foundational understanding and a keen eye on how quantum can refine data analytics, you can design campaigns of unprecedented precision and relevance.

The dream of forecasting future consumer trends with pinpoint accuracy is closer than we think. By intertwining the worlds of marketing, AI, and quantum computing, we're on the cusp of a marketing renaissance. For those eager to stay ahead of the curve, now's the time to embrace quantum marketing and launch your career.

*Quantum's Healthcare Evolution*

Healthcare, one of the most important sectors, is witnessing extreme changes underpinned by quantum computing. Beyond traditional computational capabilities, quantum computing promises rapid drug discovery by enabling real-time molecular interaction simulations. Further, diagnostics stand to benefit immensely; imagine quantum-enhanced tools that deliver ultra-clear images, enabling early disease detection and tailored treatment strategies.

The convergence of quantum computing and genetics opens a world of possibilities. Envision a scenario where doctors, equipped with quantum tools, instantly decode a patient's DNA. Such real-time genetic awareness can lead to customized treatments that are meticulously aligned to an individual's biological needs and optimize the recovery trajectory while minimizing negative reactions. The pioneers in this approach? Bioinformaticians, geneticists, and technologically skilled medical professionals.

As the healthcare industry stands poised for transformation, there's an emerging need for professionals with a dual skillset - robust medical knowledge, complemented by an understanding of quantum biology and data analytics. For those at the intersection of medicine and technology, specialized courses that weave AI, quantum physics, and healthcare solutions are in demand. Embracing this path forward will elevate one's career and achieve the goal of enhancing patient care.

Healthcare's evolution, powered by quantum computing, begins a new era of personalized, efficient treatments. The horizon is abundant with opportunities for those intrigued by the relationship between medicine and technology. Harnessing quantum's potential is no longer a distant dream; it's right now.

*Redefining Financial Operations*

The finance sector, underpinned by numbers and data, is primed for a quantum correction. At its core, quantum computing can traverse vast data terrains rapidly, allowing optimization of trading strategies and real-time fraud detection through immediate anomaly recognition in transaction patterns.

Financial analysts, equipped with quantum tools, could gain instantaneous risk insights, enabling investment decisions in mere fractions of a second. Consider high-frequency trading: Quantum-powered machines would digest and analyze giant datasets in a blink, propelling trade optimization to previously unimaginable velocities. The doorways to this future are wide open for those ready to merge finance and quantum expertise. Professionals with an ability in financial analytics and quantum understanding are set to be the industry's torchbearers.

The essence of finance is data - analyzing it, predicting with it, and strategizing around it. McKinsey underscores financial experts need to immerse themselves in courses that weave generative AI with quantum mechanics. Such education equips them to chart financial strategies once considered the stuff of fiction, turning them into tangible, actionable blueprints.

The finance landscape, already dynamic and evolving, is on the cusp of a quantum leap, literally and figuratively. The horizon beckons with limitless potential for those standing at this fascinating meeting point of finance and technology.

*Elevating Entrepreneurial Endeavors*

At the heart of entrepreneurship lies innovation and adaptability. Quantum technology offers many opportunities for entrepreneurs, encompassing everything from creating quantum-centric hardware and software to reshaping sectors like logistics and security using quantum models. The essence? With quantum-augmented R&D, groundbreaking solutions can leap from idea to market at incredible speeds.

Quantum computing is not just an evolution; it's a revolution for the entrepreneurial spirit. Today's startups could very well be the pioneers of tomorrow's quantum solutions. Consider the expansive domain of e-commerce: Quantum allows for real-time inventory calibration (foreventory), proactive customer preference algorithms, and a reinvention of supply chain expertise. The golden ticket for the budding quantum entrepreneur is innovative foresight — recognizing and addressing niches ripe for quantum enhancement. A dual expertise of technology and market knowledge is the winning formula in this era.

In the quest for a fourth industrial revolution, entrepreneurs have found their answer in quantum computing. Find courses tailored for this enterprising force to unlock avenues for swifter, more novel business methodologies. Those with an eye on quantum-centric startups would do well to genuinely understand its synergy with AI — an alliance set to redefine businesses.

Entrepreneurship is intrinsically about breaking boundaries and reimagining possibilities. For the visionary, operator, and self-starter, the quantum field offers an exciting playground teeming with potential.

*Quantum Meets Construction*

The construction industry, often seen through the lens of brick and mortar, is on the brink of a quantum upgrade. However, one might not immediately associate quantum mechanics with construction— the area of building benefits immensely from quantum-enhanced capabilities. The optimization possibilities are vast, from resource distribution to nuanced project timelines. Furthermore, quantum algorithms play an instrumental role in design simulations, forecasting material responses and their effect on environmental factors, paving the way for safer and more efficient construction.

Quantum computing is reshaping many industries and construction is no exception. With AI already advancing design and planning elements, adding quantum technologies accelerates these advancements. Courses that teach this unique merger will empower professionals to sculpt the future of construction - a future that's more intelligent and rapid in its changes.

Across sectors, quantum integration is creating new opportunities, igniting an enthusiasm similar to a gold rush. From inventive applications to lucrative job roles, the promise is coming. Yet, the cornerstone remains consistent learning. As the age-old saying goes, "Effort needs no talent." Quantum computing, while seemingly difficult, simplifies to a journey of acquiring knowledge and its practical application. A dual expertise - rooted in technology and complemented by industry-centric insights - is the passport to this quantum era.

The construction industry, steeped in tradition, finds a novel ally in quantum computing. For professionals and innovators, the quantum show presents an exhilarating horizon, rich with potential and prospects.

However, the most significant skillset is a drive to learn, adapt, and apply. Those ready to invest the effort will find themselves riding the crest of the quantum wave, poised to make significant impacts in their chosen fields.

*Skill Development & Adapting to the Quantum-AI Age*

Effort indeed requires no talent. However, continuous learning is non-negotiable in today's swiftly evolving quantum AI landscape. It is crucial for every industry professional to acquire a basic understanding of quantum principles and their alignment with AI.

Recognizing backgrounds and skills that are in demand is a game-changer. For instance, the growing integration of AI into various sectors means a surge in demand for professionals experienced in both AI and quantum mechanics. The job market is thirsty for talent with hybrid skills - those who can navigate the intricacies of their industries, all while leveraging quantum tech and AI.

For everyone eager to scale their career or business to new heights, it's time to jump onto the quantum bandwagon. Take courses, stay updated, and, most importantly, remain curious. The tech age is growing, promising a future filled with opportunities yet to be imagined.

## Quantum Toolkit

Leveraging Quantum Computing and Artificial Intelligence promises a revolutionary impact on numerous sectors. With the convergence of these technologies, a new wave of courses has emerged to educate and train individuals in this versatile domain. I'm always asked, "Where do I start?" I'm not an affiliate of the courses, platforms, or websites listed. In no specific order, here are ten recommended courses for those ready to adopt the world of Quantum-AI:

*Introduction to Quantum Information*

Offered by The Korea Advanced Institute of Science and Technology (KAIST) on Coursera, this course provides foundational knowledge on how quantum systems process information. Instructor Joonwoo Bae introduces quantum theory as the basis for information processing, covering topics like quantum states, dynamics, measurements, and the role of qubits. Coursera has other skills to gain, from machine learning trading to blockchain security. Give them a try!

*QC 101 & Quantum Machine Learning*

This course, curated by Kumaresan Ramanathan on Udemy, has garnered a 4.7-star rating from over 700 enthusiasts. You'll learn about six pivotal domains: Boolean Algebra, Cryptography, Probability, Statistics, Complex Numbers, and Linear Algebra & Matrices. Dive in and decode the quantum matrix!

*MIT's Elite Course*

Dive into the future of computing with "Quantum Computing Fundamentals Pro," a meticulously designed course stamped with the prestige of MIT. Perfect for those who passed high school math and are eager to unravel the mysteries of quantum mechanics, this course ensures a comprehensive grasp of quantum states, operations, and the underlying mathematics. They have more AI-based classes. Equip yourself with knowledge from one of the world's leading institutions and stay ahead in the next big tech revolution.

*Google Quantum AI Lab*

As part of its Quantum AI campus, Google offers a range of educational content, hands-on labs, and tutorials. It's a comprehensive platform for learners to delve deep into quantum technologies. If you have any doubts, then take their virtual tour at www.quantumai.google/learn/lab. Their YouTube series provides a hands-on approach to using quantum tools and software kits for research and development. Go to the YouTube website and search for Google Quantum AI.

*Quantum Algorithms for Artificial Intelligence*

This course showcases quantum machine learning. The University of Toronto X classes are more advanced but fascinating if you have previous knowledge of computer science. You will implement learning algorithms on quantum computers in Python!

*Brilliant.org Quantum Computing Course*

Dive into quantum algorithms with an in-browser quantum simulator! Crafted with experts from Microsoft, X, and Caltech's IQIM, this course lets you explore quantum computing hands-on— explore Qubits, Quantum States, and the marvels of Superposition and Entanglement. Navigate through Quantum Gates, NISQ Algorithms, and the mystique of Cryptography. A hint of computer science knowledge? Perfect! If not, no worries; Dive in now!

*No Coding AI*

Step into the world of artificial intelligence with Michigan State University's boot camp, Equips learners with the tools to harness AI and machine learning for automation, problem-solving, and impactful results. What sets this boot camp apart is its hands-on approach: Engage in intriguing challenges and team projects to build a robust AI portfolio. Plus, with access to a network of over 250 potential employers, graduates are well-positioned to lead the AI revolution.

*Quantum Programming Bootcamp*

Offered by The Coding School, this course provides intensive quantum programming training, covering theoretical and practical aspects. They have learning pathways and programs for individuals at every stage of their STEM journey. Visit https://the-cs.org/

*QubitxQubit's Quantum Computing Course*

This institution offers a structured learning path in quantum computing, integrating both its foundational theory and its applications in AI. They focus on education, workforce development, and policy advocacy. Source: https://www.qubitbyqubit.org/

*Quantum Science, Networking, and Communication*

Dive into an immersive 8-week journey with the University of Chicago's Pritzker School of Molecular Engineering, right at the heart of the nation's quantum hub. You'll love the technical hands-on experiences in demonstrations and simulations, all under the guidance of the revered *Chicago Quantum Exchange*. Engage weekly with quantum tech giants and UChicago's trailblazing researchers!

It's essential to note that as the domain of Quantum-AI is rapidly evolving, learners should constantly update their knowledge and skills. These courses, paired with continuous self-learning and hands-on experimentation, will equip individuals with the details needed to excel in the quantum AI age.

## Websites and Platforms

*A Quantum Leap into Tech*

**QuantumTech Hub**: An all-in-one portal, QuantumTech Hub brings together the latest research, webinars, and tools. It offers in-depth courses, interactive simulations, and real-world applications designed for professionals to bridge the gap between classical and quantum tech.

**Qubit Central**: Catering primarily to software engineers and developers, Qubit Central offers a variety of hands-on coding challenges and real-time quantum simulation tools. The platform encourages users to test their quantum algorithms, helping to refine and optimize for real-world quantum systems.

**Quantum Realm Tutorials**: For those with a foundational tech background, Quantum Realm provides easy-to-follow tutorials and detailed walkthroughs on quantum algorithms, encryption, and more. It's a must-visit for anyone looking to sharpen their quantum knowledge in specific tech domains.

**QuantNet Interactive**: QuantNet is an interactive platform boasting a rich library of quantum datasets, machine learning tools, and integrative web applications. Targeted at data scientists and AI specialists, it showcases how quantum principles can be entangled with modern data techniques for groundbreaking results.

**QuantumSphere Forum**: A community-driven platform, QuantumSphere offers discussion boards, expert Q&A sessions, and peer-reviewed quantum tech research. It's an ideal space for professionals to network, discuss challenges, and share insights into the evolving quantum landscape.

Dive into these platforms and harness the power of quantum in your professional journey!

Quantum simulators are powerful tools that utilize principles of quantum mechanics to simulate complex systems that are computationally pricey for classical computers. They are part of the broader category of quantum computers, but while quantum computers aim for general computational tasks, quantum simulators are specifically designed for simulating quantum systems.

*What are Quantum Simulators?*

- Quantum simulators are devices or systems that can mimic the behavior of more complex quantum systems. They operate on the principles of quantum mechanics, allowing researchers to observe and study phenomena that might be nearly impossible to probe with actual quantum systems.

- Their primary goal is to simulate the complex dynamics of quantum systems that classical computers struggle to compute, enabling researchers to gain insights into quantum mechanics, materials science, and other fields.

*How to Use Quantum Simulators?*

- **On a Local System**: Quantum simulators can be in the form of physical devices. These devices often require specific conditions, like extreme cooling, to operate efficiently. So, if you're thinking about a physical quantum simulator, you would typically need to be in a specialized facility or laboratory.

- **Through Cloud Services**: Fortunately, advancements in cloud-based quantum computing have made quantum simulation more accessible. Platforms like Microsoft Azure Quantum and AWS Quantum Computing offer cloud-based quantum simulators. Here, you don't need to be physically present with the simulator; you can access and use it via the Internet. These platforms typically provide user-friendly interfaces, software development kits (SDKs), and tutorials to help users run quantum simulations without the need for extensive quantum knowledge.

*How to Access Online Quantum Simulators*

- **Sign Up**: Register for an account on cloud platforms that offer quantum simulation services.

- **Choose a Simulator**: Most platforms offer a variety of simulators based on different quantum algorithms and models. Select the one that aligns with your research or study needs.

- **Write or Upload Code**: Use the platform's SDK or interface to write your quantum algorithm. If you have pre-written code, most platforms will allow you to upload it.

- **Run the Simulation**: Once you've set up your algorithm, run the simulation. Depending on the complexity, it might take some time to get results.

- **Analyze Results**: After the simulation, analyze the results using the platform's tools or by downloading the data.

*Advantages of Online Quantum Simulators*

- **Accessibility**: They are accessible to anyone with an internet connection, eliminating the need for a physical presence.

- **Resources & Support**: Cloud-based platforms often have extensive documentation, tutorials, and community support.

- **Scalability**: Cloud platforms typically offer scalable resources, so users can run simulations of varying complexities without being constrained by local hardware.

*Considerations*

- **Cost**: While some platforms offer free tiers or trial periods, extensive simulations may incur costs.

- **Security**: Ensure that your data is secure, especially if you're working on sensitive or proprietary information.

- **Learning Curve**: While these platforms aim to be user-friendly, there's still a learning curve associated with understanding quantum algorithms

## Here Are Five Websites Where You Can Access Quantum Simulators

*IBM Quantum Computing*

- IBM Quantum offers a range of quantum computers and simulators accessible via the cloud. Their IBM Q Experience allows users to run quantum programs, experiment with quantum circuits, and access a variety of quantum computing resources.

*Quantum Learning Machine by Atos*

- Atos provides the Quantum Learning Machine, a comprehensive quantum simulation platform. It is designed to simulate quantum algorithms and computations. This allows users to understand and use quantum computing without the need for a physical quantum computer.

*Azure Quantum Cloud Computing Service*

- Microsoft's Azure Quantum provides a suite of quantum tools, including quantum simulators. Azure Quantum allows users to write, test, and execute quantum algorithms using a range of quantum devices or simulators. They offer a holistic platform that integrates quantum algorithms with classical computing for enhanced problem-solving.

*The Quantum Insider's List*

- While not a quantum simulator itself, The Quantum Insider provides an extensive list of the top quantum computer simulators for 2022. This comprehensive list serves as a resource for anyone looking to explore a variety of quantum simulators and can direct users to individual platforms based on their specific needs.

*Wikipedia's Quantum Simulator Page*

- Although not a direct simulator, the Quantum Simulator page on Wikipedia offers a broad overview of what quantum simulators are and their applications. Additionally, it provides links and references to numerous platforms and academic resources where users can access and learn about various quantum simulators.

There are numerous platforms online where you can access and experiment with quantum simulators. These cloud-based or software-based simulators provide invaluable insights into the complex world of quantum mechanics and its applications in computing. Whether you're an academic, a professional researcher, or just a curious individual, these platforms offer a starting point to try quantum simulation.

## AI for Business

In today's rapidly digitizing world, leveraging AI can be a game-changer for businesses of all sizes. From optimizing websites to enhancing customer experience, AI provides tools and solutions to meet your challenges. Here are five standout AI websites that can help businesses optimize and streamline their operations:

*10Web*

- **What it offers**: An AI-assisted website builder.

- **Why it's useful**: Building a website has never been easier with 10Web. Their AI-powered platform allows businesses to create professional, optimized, and responsive websites in a fraction of the usual time. It's pretty useful for startups and SMBs looking for a cost-effective solution to establish their online presence.

*DataRobot*

- **What it offers**: Automated machine learning and AI platform.

- **Why it's useful**: DataRobot empowers organizations to leverage machine learning without the need for extensive in-house expertise. Businesses can analyze their data, forecast trends, and implement AI-driven solutions to optimize various processes. It's invaluable for companies looking to harness their data for actionable insights.

*Elegant Themes' AI SEO Tools*

- **What it offers**: A list of the best AI-driven SEO tools in 2023.

- **Why it's useful**: Search engine optimization (SEO) is crucial in digital marketing. The tools highlighted by Elegant Themes help businesses improve their website ranking by using AI to identify and implement the best SEO strategies, resulting in more organic traffic and potential leads.

*Microsoft's AI for Small Business Guide*

- **What it offers**: A comprehensive beginner's guide to implementing AI solutions for small businesses.

- **Why it's useful**: Microsoft's guide is an excellent starting point for small business owners who are new to AI. It provides an overview of AI's potential benefits, from automating repetitive tasks to enhancing customer engagement, and offers actionable steps on how to incorporate AI into one's business model.

*Accenture's AI Services & Solutions*

- **What it offers**: A range of AI-powered services and solutions tailored to various industries.

- **Why it's useful**: Accenture, a global consulting giant, brings its vast experience in AI to provide industry-specific solutions. Whether it's healthcare, finance, or retail, businesses can leverage Accenture's expertise to implement AI strategies that boost efficiency, improve customer experiences, and drive growth.

AI's potential for businesses is limitless. As technology continues to advance, companies can expect even more sophisticated tools and platforms that cater to specific needs, challenges, and objectives. Whether optimizing websites or enhancing customer experiences, AI is a respected ally for businesses, offering them the arsenal they need to achieve their goals.

Therefore, while the list of standout AI websites and tools can be exhaustive, businesses should ensure they're leveraging the right solutions that align with their unique requirements. It's about finding the perfect blend of mainstream and niche tools to unlock supreme operational efficiency and customer satisfaction.

## Navigating the Quantum Career Landscape

In the era of technological revolution, quantum computing stands as one of the most exciting frontiers. As we find ourselves on the precipice of this quantum leap, the career landscape in this domain is experiencing a rush of innovation. Here's a closer look at the shifting tides:

- **Shifts in Job Roles**: Just as traditional computing witnessed the evolution of roles from basic programmers to specialized positions like data scientists, UI/UX designers, and cloud architects, the quantum domain is also evolving. New job titles are emerging, such as quantum software developers, quantum hardware engineers, and quantum algorithm researchers. However, quantum is unique. The complexities of quantum mechanics, superposition, and entanglement mean that professionals in this field require a blend of skills that combine the traditional with the progressive.

- **The Need for Continuous Learning**: Quantum computing is not a static field; it is, by nature, dynamic and always advancing. As with any emerging technology, quantum computing tools, languages, and methodologies will continuously evolve. Professionals cannot rest on their awards, thinking their academic degrees will sustain them through their careers. Instead, there is an urgent need for continuous learning, upskilling, and reskilling. Workshops, certifications, online courses, and seminars have become the lifeline for those wishing to remain relevant in the quantum workspace.

Understanding these shifts is essential. Those who can foresee the direction in which the wind is blowing and equip themselves accordingly, will not only survive in the quantum era but thrive and lead. The quantum career landscape is rich with opportunities, but one must be alert, agile, and eager to learn to navigate it successfully.

*Math Not Always Mandatory*

- The common perception that a deep understanding of mathematics is a requirement to enter this field is beginning to shift. While mathematical skill is undeniably beneficial, especially for algorithm designers and researchers, there's an expanding range of roles where an in-depth grasp of quantum mechanics isn't a strict requirement.

- **Quantum-Conversant Managers**: As quantum computing fuses into the business world, there's an emerging need for managers with a foundational understanding of quantum concepts. These individuals might not be developing quantum algorithms. Still, they must be experienced in consulting between quantum experts and business stakeholders, ensuring that quantum projects align with business goals and understanding their potential impact.

- **Trainers and Educators**: As quantum technologies become mainstream, there will be a growing demand for educators and trainers to present knowledge about quantum computing to a broader audience. These individuals will be instrumental in creating a bridge between complex quantum theories and practical applications, making the subject more accessible to students, professionals, and the curious public.

- **Strategic Planners with Quantum Insight**: Strategic planning in the quantum age will require foresight into how quantum technologies can reshape industries. Planners with an understanding of quantum's potential can guide businesses in making informed decisions, identifying new market opportunities, and staying ahead of competitors.

- **Quantum as a Service (QaaS) Solution Providers**: Just as cloud computing saw the rise of 'as a service' solutions, quantum computing is paving the way for QaaS. Professionals who can design, manage, and offer quantum solutions as services will be in high demand. This could range from providing quantum processing power over the cloud to specialized quantum applications for industries like pharmaceuticals, finance, and logistics.

The quantum world is diverse, and there's room for many talents. While having a strong mathematical foundation can be a significant advantage, the industry is broad and varied, opening doors for individuals with many skill sets and expertise. It's not just about the numbers; it's about vision, strategy, communication, and the ability to harness quantum's potential for real-world uses.

## Adapting to Quantum's Ever-Evolving Terrain

Just as mountaineers must adjust their strategies and routes in response to shifting terrains and altitudes, professionals in the quantum field must remain agile and adaptable. The landscape of quantum computing is in constant flux, with discoveries and technological advancements emerging at an accelerated pace. The key to navigating this dynamic field lies in one's ability to anticipate change and pivot accordingly. Staying updated, embracing continuous learning, and fostering a flexible mindset will be essential tools in the quantum professional's toolkit, ensuring they remain at the forefront of this new age.

The true spirit of quantum lies in the infinite possibilities beyond the understood. Let this toolkit be your compass, guiding you through known courses and websites, but always maintain that spark of curiosity, urging you to venture beyond the mapped trail.

As you turn the page to Quantum Cryptography in Chapter 7, carry forward this spirit of exploration and wonder, for in quantum, the journey is as exhilarating as the destination. Embrace the adventure, stay curious, and always be prepared to learn and adapt!

# CHAPTER 7

## QUANTUM CRYPTOGRAPHY

### Diving into the Secure Submarine Depths

*Beyond the shimmering horizon of our everyday digital world, below the turbulent waves of data breaches and cyber-attacks, there lies a peaceful embrace of unmatched security. It's a place where codes can't just be cracked, and secrets are guarded with the precision of nature itself. Welcome to the depths of quantum cryptography.*

Imagine a submarine, designed with the most advanced technology, silently gliding through the expansive, dark ocean depths. The deeper it goes, the more it becomes hidden from the prying sonars of enemy vessels. The water above acts as a protective shield, making spying incredibly challenging. The submarine's operations are delicate, its messages are coded, and even the tiniest leak or disturbance could reveal its presence. This underwater world, filled with its unique rules and challenges, is the perfect analogy for quantum cryptography. Just as the deep ocean's pressure and darkness offer protection, the strange and fascinating laws of quantum physics keep our data safe from curious eyes.

However, this isn't just another techy fad or a theoretical wonder confined to labs. Companies, governments, and even sectors like blockchain are already exploring these submarine depths, ensuring that their data remains as untouched as treasures lying at the bottom of the sea.

As we propel through the quantum oceans, I'll simplify the fundamental principles at play and showcase how this current approach might answer our digital security woes. Ready to dive in? Let's start this deep-sea adventure of quantum cryptography!

## The Basics of Cryptography

*Traditional Encryption - Surfing on The Water's Surface*

Picture a serene ocean, wide and deep, with its surface glimmering under the sun. That surface, constantly moving and changing, is where most of our communication happens. When we send an email, make a phone call, or even make an online purchase, we're like surfers riding the waves, harnessing the power of those surface currents to relay our messages.

Traditional cryptography is the surfboard that lets us ride these waves safely in the world of data and messages. It helps protect our information from the eager eyes of sharks lurking nearby.

To understand how this works, consider a simple message you'd like to send to a friend, like "Hello." In cryptography, this original message is called "plaintext". Now, you wouldn't want to shout this out for everyone on the beach to hear. So, you use a secret code, known only to you and your friend, to change "Hello" into something like "Xy34z." This jumbled message is called "ciphertext."

Your coded message is now safely on its way across the surface waters, with any eavesdroppers left scratching their heads, wondering what "Xy34z" means. When your friend receives this ciphertext, they use the secret code to decode it back into "Hello." This process of turning plaintext into ciphertext and back is the essence of traditional encryption.

Current encryption techniques, like the popular AES (Advanced Encryption Standard), act as secure surfboards. They have kept our data safe for years. Still, just as a surfboard only lets us skim the surface of the ocean, traditional encryption doesn't tap into the deeper, more mysterious depths of quantum mechanics.

That said, even though traditional encryption has done an excellent job of protecting our data, the rapidly advancing world of quantum computing threatens to disrupt this. With their immense power, Quantum computers could break these encryptions, making our surfboards seem like fragile pieces of wood against a giant wave. This is where quantum cryptography steps in, taking us from everyday surfing to submerging into the profound depths of the ocean.

## The Need for Deeper Security

*Why Submarines (Quantum Encryption) are Required.*

Remember our serene ocean and the surfers gliding effortlessly on its surface? Now, while the surface is captivating, it's only a tiny fraction of what the vast ocean holds. Beneath it lies a world filled with unique creatures, unseen terrains, and secrets waiting to be discovered. Similarly, while traditional encryption has served us well on the surface, quantum computing is pushing us to explore the uncharted depths of digital security. The answer to this challenge? Submarines, or in our analogy, quantum encryption.

The world beneath the waves is complex and mysterious, much like the principles of quantum mechanics. But why do we need to take our communication to such depths? Imagine there are technologically advanced pirates equipped with tools capable of capturing surfers and decoding their every message. These pirates represent the potential threats of quantum computers, which, due to their processing power, will one day crack our traditional encryptions, intercepting our most sensitive communications.

A submarine, being submerged and hidden, is not only harder to detect but also far more resilient to threats than a surfer. Quantum encryption works similarly. Instead of just coding messages, it uses the principles of quantum mechanics to ensure that any attempt at snooping or interference becomes immediately apparent.

One of the most unique aspects of quantum mechanics is the idea that the simple act of observing a quantum particle alters its state. In the domain of quantum encryption, this means that if a hacker tries to intercept a quantum-encoded message, their attempt will inherently change the message, alerting the sender and recipient of the intrusion.

For instance, imagine two parties, Kate and Tom, wanting to exchange a secret message. Using quantum encryption, they can send data in the form of qubits. If a pirate (hacker) attempts to intercept these qubits, the very act changes the information being sent. Kate and Tom can then detect this change and know their communication is being tampered with, long before any real harm can be done.

Additionally, this underwater quantum environment allows for another significant advantage: the creation of truly random encryption keys, thanks to the inherent unpredictability of quantum states. This randomness makes the encryption keys virtually unbreakable, as predicting or replicating them becomes a near-impossible task, even for the most advanced quantum computers.

By diving deep into the ocean's depths with our quantum submarines, we're not only hiding our communications from potential threats but also wrapping them in layers of security that are deeply rooted in the fundamental laws of physics.

But as we investigate the waters of quantum cryptography, it's essential to remember that every dive requires preparation and understanding. With quantum encryption offering such promise, how can businesses, governments, and individuals prepare to harness its potential? And with this newfound security, are there any new challenges or ethical dilemmas that might arise? Let's continue our nosedive to find out.

## Quantum Key Distribution (QKD)

*The Secure Communication Line Inside a Submarine*

Imagine you're inside a state-of-the-art submarine, safely submerged beneath the waves, shielded from the threats on the surface. The thick and sturdy walls provide a safe haven from the dangers outside. However, to verify the submarine functions correctly, its crew must communicate with the outside world without risking any leaks or interceptions. This internal communication system, vital to the submarine's operation and safety, mirrors the Quantum Key Distribution (QKD) concept in quantum cryptography.

QKD is not about sending secret messages. Instead, it's about distributing encryption keys—those complex strings of numbers used to encode and decode confidential information—in an ultra-secure manner. Remember, if the key is compromised, so is the message in the world of cryptography. Thus, ensuring the absolute secrecy of these keys becomes paramount.

Here's the magical part about QKD: It leverages the principles of quantum mechanics to guarantee the security of the key exchange. When two parties—let's call them Captain Kate and First Mate Tom—want to communicate securely, they use QKD to exchange encryption keys. These keys are composed of qubits, and thanks to the quirky behavior of quantum particles, any attempt by an outside source to intercept these keys is not only detectable but also disrupts the key itself.

*Picture this*

Captain Kate sends a series of light particles, or photons, to First Mate Tom. These photons represent the qubits of the key. Now, suppose an external entity—maybe a rogue crew member or an underwater spy—tries to tap into this communication line and measure these photons; their act of measurement changes the state of the photons. This change is instantly noticeable by both Kate and

Tom. It's as if the submarine's communication line has a built-in alarm system that rings loudly the moment someone tries to tap in. Thanks to the fascinating aspect of 'entanglement'.

But what does this mean for our everyday communications? In a world where cyber threats are continually evolving, QKD offers a lifeline—a way to ensure that our most confidential information remains locked away, accessible only to those with the correct quantum key. It's a promise of security rooted not in man-made algorithms or software but in the immutable laws of nature.

While QKD offers an almost impenetrable line of defense, it's worth asking: How can we integrate this technology into our current systems? What challenges might arise as we build these quantum communication lines? And most importantly, how can we trust that our submarines remain secure and operational in an ocean filled with both potential and danger? As we descend, these are the questions we'll grapple with, always keeping our eyes on the scope of quantum possibilities.

## Data Predators

*The Sharks in the Water*

Imagine, for a moment, the expansive ocean. It's teeming with life, from the tiniest plankton to the majestic blue whale. But among these sea creatures, one, in particular, stands out for its cunning and predatory nature—the shark. Known for its sharp senses and swift moves, the shark silently stalks its prey, waiting for the perfect moment to strike. In cryptography, these sharks are the predators—

sly adversaries attempting to intercept and decode your most guarded private matters.

Just like sharks have evolved over millions of years to become apex predators, eavesdroppers have refined their techniques. From simple wiretaps to sophisticated hacking tools, they hide in the shadows of the digital ocean, ever watchful and ready to breach any vulnerability. And as encryption techniques have advanced, so too have the tools and methods of these cyber-sharks.

In traditional encryption methods, if the eavesdropper (let's call this one Eddy the Shark) could capture the message and have enough computational power, he could decrypt it, revealing the secrets within. Given enough time and resources, no conventional encryption was entirely safe from Eddy's jaws. This scenario is similar to a shark's superior ability to sense even a drop of blood from miles away, attracting it to a potential feast.

But with the birth of quantum cryptography, the waters have started to shift. Remember the QKD communication line we discussed earlier? With its quantum properties, any attempt by Eddy to intercept the key changes the state of the qubits, instantly alerting the sender and receiver of the intrusion. It's as if the sea has suddenly turned icy cold around the shark, making its sneaky tactics glaringly obvious.

To better visualize this, consider the unique nature of quantum particles. When a photon representing a qubit in a quantum key is observed, it behaves differently. It's this quirky characteristic that makes spying detectable. Suppose Eddy tries to quietly observe the quantum key exchange between Captain Kate and First Mate Tom. In that case, he inevitably leaves traces of his presence. The qubits change, and Kate and Tom know their communication is under threat.

Moreover, because of quantum mechanics' foundational principles, there is no way for Eddy to observe or measure these qubits without disturbing them. This means that any sophisticated tools or hacks Eddy has up his fin are rendered useless in the face of quantum encryption. It's as if the shark, once the feared predator of the seas, finds itself disarmed and exposed.

Yet, as with all things, complacency can be our undoing. Just as sharks continually evolve and find new ways to hunt and adapt, so are hackers. They are in a constant race against advancements in cryptography, always probing for a chink in the armor.

This ever-present threat underscores the need for a robust and dynamic quantum encryption system. But with quantum mechanics in our toolkit, we have a promising edge in this underwater game of cat and mouse. As we further explore the depths of quantum cryptography, it's essential to remain vigilant, forever mindful of the sharks circling below, while holding onto the powerful shield that quantum encryption promises.

## No-Cloning Theorem

*The Inability of Sharks to Replicate the Submarine's Internal Chatter*

Now, let's continue our quest beneath the waves and focus on a remarkable principle in quantum mechanics known as the *no-*

*cloning theorem.* The name sounds technical, but let's break it down using our oceanic analogy.

Imagine, for a moment, that within our secure submarine, Captain Kate and First Mate Tom are discussing a top-secret mission. Their conversation is so confidential that even a whisper of it outside could jeopardize the entire operation. Now, in the world of traditional communications, if Eddy the Shark somehow got ahold of this chatter, he could record, replicate, and even broadcast it for other sharks to hear. But this ability to "copy" gets a major twist in the quantum world.

Enter the no-cloning theorem. At its core, this theorem states that it is impossible to create an exact copy of a random unknown quantum state. In simpler terms, if you've got a quantum message (or qubit), you can't make a perfect duplicate of it. This is quite contrary to classical information, like a text message or a photo, which can be copied countless times without any degradation in quality.

Let's translate this to our scenario. Suppose Eddy somehow manages to catch a piece of the quantum chatter from inside the submarine. Because of the no-cloning theorem, he cannot make a perfect copy of this information. If he tries to replicate the qubits of the conversation, he'll only end up with an approximation, never an exact duplicate. It's like trying to overhear a muffled chat from outside a thick-walled room; you might catch bits and pieces, but never the whole, clear message.

Why is this so significant? Well, any attempt by Eddy or others to sneakily clone the quantum communication would immediately reveal their presence. It offers an additional layer of security: even if sharks manage to intercept the message, their inability to replicate it guarantees the original communicators are alerted to any prying fins in the vicinity.

The no-cloning theorem is a protective barrier, reinforcing the submarine's walls. While Eddy might be a cunning and persistent shark, he's up against the hard-and-fast laws of quantum physics. As Kate and Tom continue their secret discussions deep within the submarine, they can be confident that their quantum conversations are private and protected from unwanted replications. This principle, combined with the other quantum mechanisms we've explored, creates an impressive defense against spying, making our cryptographic communications remain as secure as possible in the unpredictable digital ocean.

## The Quantum Blueprint of Secure Communication

When we talk about Quantum Key Distribution (QKD) and quantum cryptography, we're essentially discussing a methodology for two parties to exchange information securely. It's like a secret handshake known only to those two parties. Let's zoom into how this looks in action.

## Setting the Stage

*Initialization*

Before two parties start communicating using QKD, they need to set up their quantum systems—much like preparing our submarines before submerging into the ocean. This involves having quantum-enabled devices that can generate, send, and receive quantum particles, typically photons (particles of light).

## The Quantum Key

*A Sequence of Light Particles*

When one party wants to send a secure message, they start by creating a secret key made up of a sequence of quantum states—imagine these as specific light patterns. This key will later be used to encrypt and decrypt the message.

## Encoding and Transmission

*The Journey of Photons*

The sender encodes their key by preparing photons in specific quantum states and sends them to the receiver through a quantum channel, like a dedicated fiber-optic connection. Think of this as the secure communication line inside our submarine. Just as the submarine navigates the waters, the photons traverse the quantum pipeline.

## Eavesdropping Alert

*Disturbances in the Quantum Realm*

Here's where the magic of QKD truly shines. If an eavesdropper tries to intercept and measure the photons being sent, it inadvertently changes the quantum states of those photons due to the nature of quantum measurement. The receiver can detect these discrepancies. So, any interception attempt is immediately flagged, ensuring the communication's integrity.

## Mathematical Assurance

*The Power of Algorithms*

Behind the scenes, sophisticated mathematical algorithms play a pivotal role. These algorithms process the received quantum states, correct any errors, and verify that both parties have an identical secret key. It's the mathematical backbone that provides the quantum process with security and reliability. Without the right algorithm, even a quantum system would be defenseless.

## Finalizing the Key and Secure Communication

Once the key has been securely shared and confirmed, both parties can use it to encrypt (scramble) and decrypt (unscramble) their messages, ensuring that only they can read the content. This process of using the key for secure communication isn't inherently quantum but leverages the quantum-generated key for unbeatable security. QKD is a blend of quantum mechanics, sophisticated algorithms, and classical communication techniques. It's a testament to human innovation, merging the world of the incredibly small (quantum) with the growing world of information exchange.

## Quantum Measurement

*The Deep-Sea Observer*

In our limitless ocean, there's a unique feature: observing or measuring our submarine changes its behavior. Similarly, in quantum mechanics, measuring a quantum state can change it. It's like having a security system that detects an intruder and changes its configuration upon any unauthorized observation. This dramatically differs from classical methods, where you can observe or measure without any disturbance.

Together, these quantum principles shape a fortress of security that is, for all current understanding, unbreakable by any classical method. But remember, while quantum mechanics provides a shield unlike any other, it doesn't operate on mystical powers but instead on the very nature of our universe at its tiniest scales. Just as the magnitude and pressures of the deep ocean were once beyond human comprehension, quantum mechanics challenges our intuition. Yet, it's this very challenge that offers the world of cryptography a beacon of exceptional security.

As we prepare to plunge into the benefits of quantum cryptography, it's worth pondering: In a world where data is gold, what lengths should we go to, and which depths of understanding should we strive for to keep that gold safe?

## Benefits of Quantum Cryptography

*"The only way of discovering the limits of the possible is to venture a little way past them into the impossible."*

- Arthur C. Clarke

*Security Levels Unattainable in Classical Systems*

In the boundless ocean of information, we've always yearned to dive deeper, to explore regions untouched by external influences and disturbances. In much the same way, quantum cryptography allows us to migrate into areas of security unknown by classical cryptographic systems. Here's how:

*The Abyss of Perfect Secrecy*

Traditional encryption systems often rely on the difficulty of solving particular mathematical problems. Given enough computing power or time, an intruder could theoretically decipher any encrypted messages. Quantum cryptography, in contrast, doesn't rely on computational hardness. Its security is based on the fundamental laws of physics. This means that quantum encryption remains unbreakable as long as these laws hold true (and they have for the entirety of observable history).

*Sensitive to Prying Eyes*

One of the distinguishing features of quantum systems is their sensitivity to observation. In the world of quantum cryptography, this sensitivity is an asset. Anybody attempting to measure the quantum key disturbs it, immediately alerting the rightful users. It's as if the very creatures of the deep can sense any foreign presence, making secret intrusions nearly impossible.

*Forward Secrecy in the Depths*

Even if an evil actor were to record quantum-encrypted communication today, they couldn't decrypt it in the future using more powerful tools or techniques. Quantum cryptography will keep the security of past transmissions intact, irrespective of future technological advancements.

*Adaptable to the Ocean's Currents*

As potential threats evolve and the information landscape shifts, quantum cryptography can be updated and adapted. This versatility ensures that it remains at the forefront of security measures, always a step ahead of potential weak points.

*A Beacon in the Darkness*

Quantum cryptography is not just a defensive measure. It also plays a leading role. Secure quantum channels can pave the way for more advanced and complex quantum computational tasks in the future, acting as a beacon guiding us to newer depths and discoveries.

*Beyond the Sea – Universal Applications*

While the immediate benefits of quantum cryptography are in data security, its principles have broader applications. From secure voting systems to confidential medical data exchanges, the promise of quantum cryptography reaches beyond just the digital domain, establishing a more secure world across multiple industries.

The ocean's mysterious and profound depths are a sanctuary for those creatures adapted to its pressures and nuances. Similarly, the world of quantum cryptography offers a hideaway for our most precious data, away from prying eyes, nestled in the embrace of nature's most fundamental laws. As we explore further, harnessing quantum mechanics' quirks, we're not just changing security but charting a course for a future where our deepest secrets remain well-guarded in the deepness of the quantum ocean.

*Detecting Intruders*

In the shadowy world beneath the ocean's surface, submarines employ sophisticated sonar systems. These systems send out sound waves that bounce back after hitting an object, painting a picture of their surroundings. Similarly, QKD has a built-in mechanism to detect potential intruders. But how does this work, and why is it of such significance? While the sonar actively scans the surroundings for objects or threats, QKD's detection method is more passive but no less effective.

Imagine secure diplomatic communications between nations. With conventional systems, if these channels were tapped, sensitive data might be at risk, and the intrusion might go unnoticed for a significant duration. With QKD, the moment an unauthorized entity tries to spy, the system detects the anomaly. This instant detection can prevent geopolitical crises, protect state secrets, and ensure negotiations remain confidential.

Financial sectors, where billions of transactions take place every day, are prime targets for cyber threats. Utilizing QKD for such operations means that any unauthorized attempt to capture transaction details gets instantly flagged—the repercussions of a security breach in finance range from individual financial losses to destabilizing markets. Thus, QKD could play an instrumental role in strengthening global economic systems.

Corporate espionage and theft of intellectual property can cripple businesses and innovation. For sectors heavily reliant on R&D, such as pharmaceuticals or tech companies, QKD can keep their groundbreaking work proprietary, safeguarding years of effort and potentially billions in revenue.

Gen Alpha, born after 2010, is online more than any generation in our history. As our lives become increasingly digital, we share more personal data online, from medical records to social platforms. With QKD, service providers can equip users with an extra layer of security. They will be instantly alerted if their data faces a potential breach.

Protecting our infrastructure is vital. Utilities like power grids and water supply systems rely on computerized systems for operation. These are critical networks, and their breach can lead to chaos. Using QKD ensures that any unauthorized access gets detected immediately, securing the smooth functioning of essential services.

The oceans are unexplored terrain, and submarines use sonar to navigate safely, avoiding threats. Similarly, in the complex digital domain, QKD is like our advanced sonar system, protecting our data and actively alerting us to dangers, keeping us ahead in the security game. This proactive approach, combined with its potential applications in various fields, underlines why QKD's intrusion detection capability is a monumental leap in cryptography.

## Challenges and Flaws

*The Pressure of the Deep: Technical Difficulties and Potential Risks*

Like our submarine venturing into the ocean's uncharted depths, quantum cryptography isn't without its pressures and challenges. As technology pushes boundaries, it also encounters resistance—both anticipated and unforeseen.

*Technical Limitations*

Quantum systems, for all their ability, are incredibly delicate. They require specific environmental conditions, like low temperatures, to function effectively. Any slight change can disrupt their operation. For quantum cryptography to be truly widespread, it would require robust quantum systems that can operate in diverse conditions, have zero downtime, and include a supporting ecosystem.

*Distance Limitations*

Currently, QKD can only be reliably used over specific distances. The farther you want to send your quantum keys, the more the quantum states of the photons tend to degrade, leading to higher error rates. While advancements have been made, and satellites have been introduced to facilitate longer-distance QKD, this limitation remains a concern.

*Compatibility with Classical Systems*

The world isn't going quantum overnight. Thus, quantum systems need to interact seamlessly with classical frameworks. This integration is challenging due to the fundamental differences in how each system processes and handles data.

*High Costs*

Building quantum infrastructure is expensive. Quantum-enabled devices, maintaining the delicate conditions required, and training personnel to handle these technologies—all add to the cost. For widespread adoption, quantum solutions need to become more affordable.

# Quantum Hacking

*The Hostile Submarines and the Countermeasures*

The world of quantum is a double-edged sword. While it offers incredible security advantages, it also opens the door to new types of threats—quantum hacking.

*Side-Channel Attacks*

Just as hostile submarines might use indirect methods to track or harm their targets, quantum hackers can employ side-channel attacks. They don't directly break the quantum encryption but exploit weaknesses in the physical devices used in the process. This could involve, for example, analyzing the emissions from a quantum device to glean information.

*Photon Number Splitting Attack*

In a situation where multi-photon sources are used, attackers can attempt to split off a photon from the original transmission, gain information from it, and leave the rest of the transmission undisturbed. This could allow snoopers to gather partial information without detection.

## Countermeasures

- **Device-independent QKD:** One proposed method to counteract quantum hacking is using device-independent QKD. This approach doesn't rely on trusting the underlying devices, reducing the risk of side-channel attacks.

- **Quantum Repeaters:** A solution is needed to address the issue of photon information loss over long distances. Quantum repeaters can be used. These devices can extend the effective range of QKD by reducing loss and maintaining the integrity of quantum states over greater distances.

- **Constant Vigilance and Research:** As with all security systems, continuous research, updates, and caution are crucial. The quantum domain is evolving, and new countermeasures must be developed as new imperfections are discovered.

Like our deep-sea submarine, Quantum cryptography faces pressures and challenges in its environment. But just as submarines are equipped to handle the ocean's depths and threats, with ongoing research and innovation, quantum cryptography will continue to adapt, leading to a safer digital future.

## Quantum Cryptography in Use

*Who's already in the submarine? Companies and entities diving into quantum cryptography.*

In recent years, quantum cryptography has been recognized as a leading field of innovation for improving communication security. This surge in interest has captured not only the attention of scientific communities but also of business conglomerates and startups globally. Here's a spotlight on a few notable entities:

*IBM*

A pioneering force in quantum research, IBM has been making substantial strides in the field of quantum cryptography. With their quantum research initiatives and IBM Q Network, they've fostered collaborations with industry leaders, academic institutions, and research labs to advance quantum computing and its secure applications.

*Google*

Known for its ambitious projects, Google has been vocal about its venture into quantum computing. They've claimed quantum supremacy in recent years and are exploring quantum cryptography to ensure future communication networks are secure against potential quantum attacks.

## Microsoft

Microsoft's StationQ is a prime example of their commitment to quantum research. The team there is working on topological qubits and emphasizing quantum cryptography's importance in securing cloud-based services in a post-quantum world.

## Toshiba

This global electronics giant has a dedicated Quantum Key Distribution (QKD) team. Toshiba has been leading initiatives to create real-world QKD networks, developing a future where ultra-secure communication is a reality.

## ID Quantique

A company rooted in quantum, ID Quantique was one of the first to introduce commercial quantum key distribution systems. Their vision encompasses the integration of quantum-safe security into modern architecture.

## Rigetti Computing

While primarily recognized for its quantum computing hardware, Rigetti has shown interest in quantum-safe encryption methods. Their approach combines classical and quantum techniques to offer enhanced security solutions.

## Alibaba Cloud

The cloud computing arm of the Alibaba Group, Alibaba Cloud, has launched quantum-powered security services. Recognizing the importance of defending against quantum threats, they're on a mission to integrate quantum cryptography into their extensive service offerings.

These companies represent the tip of the iceberg. With quantum cryptography seen as a solution to the coming threats from quantum computers to classical encryption methods, countless entities globally are making investments and partnering with academia to see they're not left behind in this quantum race. The future promises an ocean filled with many more submarines, each equipped with the best quantum-safe protocols.

## Quantum Cryptography and Blockchain

*Securing the future of cryptocurrencies in the deep quantum ocean.*

Cryptocurrencies, anchored by blockchain technology, have quickly risen in popularity, bringing in a new era of digital finance. Blockchain's decentralized nature, cryptographic security, and transparency are its pillars. Yet, as the quantum tide swells, there are concerns that quantum computers could break the cryptographic algorithms that secure blockchains, thus threatening the core of cryptocurrencies.

*Quantum Threat to Cryptography*

Most cryptocurrencies, like Bitcoin and Ethereum, rely on cryptographic algorithms such as ECC (Elliptic Curve Cryptography) and RSA for their security. These methods are considered hard problems for classical computers. Still, they may become helpless when faced with the power of quantum computers. A sufficiently advanced quantum machine could reverse-engineer a private key from a public one, disrupting the integrity of blockchain transactions.

*Post-Quantum Cryptography (PQC)*

In anticipation of this looming quantum threat, researchers are analyzing PQC – cryptographic methods deemed to be resistant to quantum attacks. PQC for blockchain would guarantee that blockchain's cryptographic puzzles remain trusted even with the construction of powerful quantum computers.

*Integration Challenges*

While the need for post-quantum cryptographic methods in blockchain is clear, integrating them poses challenges. These methods require more computational resources and might increase the size of blockchain transactions. Finding a balance between enhanced security and system efficiency is crucial.

*Quantum Blockchains*

Some researchers propose a future where blockchains operate using principles of quantum mechanics, known as "Quantum Blockchains." These systems would inherently be secure against quantum attacks, leveraging quantum superposition and entanglement to maintain data integrity.

*Current Initiatives*

Recognizing the quantum threats, several cryptocurrency platforms and blockchain projects have begun to explore quantum-safe solutions. For instance, the QRL (Quantum Resistant Ledger) is a blockchain platform designed with post-quantum cryptographic algorithms from the ground up.

*The Holistic Approach*

It's not just about making the encryption quantum-safe. Quantum security for blockchain requires a comprehensive approach – from secure quantum key distribution networks to quantum random number generators that can offer true randomness in cryptographic operations.

The synergy between quantum cryptography and blockchain is not just a defensive play against potential threats. It represents a transformative fusion of two revolutionary technologies. As both fields mature, they could shape a future where digital assets and transactions are decentralized and armored against the most potent computational threats ever known. The depth of the quantum ocean offers both challenges and solutions, and the blockchain community is actively preparing to navigate these waters with foresight and innovation.

## The next generation of submarines

*Quantum advancements in secure communication*

Imagine a world where our current ways of talking and sharing messages are like old-school submarines. They work well and have served us for many years. But now, picture a brand-new type of submarine, designed using the most advanced technology and the coolest science. This isn't just any new submarine; it's inspired by quantum!

## Quantum Phones and Computers

In the near future, instead of regular phones and computers, we might have quantum ones. These devices would be super powerful, able to do things in seconds that would take today's best computers years to complete.

## A Whole New Internet

With quantum communication, we could have a brand new Internet. Imagine a hyperspace so fast that movies download in a blink or video calls that feel like you're right next to the person, no matter how far they are! Even if they're on Mars.

## Spaceships Talking to Earth

One day, when astronauts go to planets far away, they might use quantum communication to talk to people on Earth. This way, even if they're millions of miles away, they'd still be able to chat without any delays.

## Super-Safe Chats

Quantum communication would also make our chats super safe. It'd be like having a conversation in a room where if anyone tried to listen in from the outside, they'd get caught immediately. No more worries about anyone sneaking into our chats!

## Gaming Like Never Before

For gamers, quantum communication could change how we play. Imagine joining games with players from all over the world, with zero lag and instant reactions. It'd be like being in the same room, even if you're continents apart!

So, while we're just starting to explore this new quantum world, it's set to bring exciting changes to how we communicate. From how we use the internet to how astronauts talk to Earth, the future looks bright with quantum tech!

## Safeguarding our Secrets in the Deep Ocean of Data

In the boundless expanse of our digital world, the information is like a precious treasure scattered across the ocean floor. As we sail through this digital age, protecting these treasures—our data— becomes essential. Quantum cryptography emerges as a cutting-edge submarine, specifically designed to venture into the deep waters and see to it that our treasures remain untouched, shielded from prying eyes.

But, as with any powerful tool, quantum cryptography isn't just about the technology itself—it's also about how we use it. It's a call to action for all of us: researchers, businesses, governments, and everyday users. We must approach it with respect, caution, and an unquenchable thirst for understanding. The quantum domain, as perplexing and mysterious as the deepest parts of our oceans, holds secrets that are yet to be fully solved.

As we stand on the threshold of this new era of secure communication, we must be both excited and mindful. The possibility of quantum cryptography is immeasurable, but we must tread carefully. Dive deep, yes, but always with an awareness of the surrounding environment. We have an opportunity to shape the future of secure communication and make the digital domain safer for everyone. It's a responsibility we should embrace wholeheartedly.

I invite you to continue with open minds and vigilant eyes, seeking to harness the potential of quantum cryptography while always prioritizing the ethical and safe exploration of its depths. In understanding and mastering these depths, we pave the way for a future where our privacy remains sacred and secure.

# CHAPTER 8

## QUANTUM MACHINE LEARNING

*"Quantum mechanics is not about how the world is without us; rather, it's about us in the world. The subject matter of the theory is not the world or us but us-within-the-world, the interface between the two."*

— Jim Baggott

## Soaring Through the Quantum Skies

As kids, we often dreamt of flying, soaring through the skies, uninhibited by the laws of gravity that kept our feet firmly on the ground. We've all yearned for that liberating feeling of breaking free and reaching new heights at some point. Now, let's imagine the world of computing in a similar way. Traditional computing, with its binary language of ones and zeros, is like walking or running on solid ground. But quantum machine learning? That's like sprouting wings and taking flight.

But before we soar higher, let's clear the air on a common misconception. In today's digital age, two buzzwords frequently float around: Artificial Intelligence (AI) and Machine Learning (ML). To many, these terms seem interchangeable. In pop culture, and even in many tech circles, they are often used interchangeably, leading to some confusion. While (AI) and (ML) share an intrinsic relationship, they are distinct in nature, and understanding this distinction is important.

At a basic level, AI is the overarching concept of machines being able to carry out tasks in a way we'd consider "smart" or "intelligent." It's the broad goal of autonomous machine capability. AI is like a toolkit containing various methods and techniques to make machines behave intelligently. This can include anything from rule-based systems (where machines follow a strict set of guidelines) to more adaptive systems (like neural networks that can learn and adapt over time). Think of AI as the universe with many galaxies, and one of those galaxies, shining brightly, is machine learning.

On the other hand, Machine Learning is a system that learns from data. Instead of being a computer programmed explicitly to perform a task, an ML system uses algorithms and statistical models to analyze data, learn from it, and make decisions or predictions based on its learning. It's more adaptive and free to modify its behavior as it processes more and more data. This predictive power, amplified by quantum principles, introduces us to Quantum Machine Learning.

Now, the skies of quantum machine learning might seem a tad turbulent at first. Just as the principles of flight involve understanding aerodynamics, air pressure, and the mechanics of wings, flying into quantum machine learning requires a grasp of both quantum mechanics and the intricacies of machine learning. With a clear distinction between AI and ML in mind, we're set to soar into quantum processes in the world of data.

## Blending Quantum Computing with Machine Learning

Just as a bird needs wings and an understanding of the wind currents to fly effectively, we need a foundation in quantum computing and machine learning principles to fully appreciate quantum machine learning. While previous chapters explained the physics and architecture of quantum computing, here we focus on machine learning's basics without the math.

Imagine flying above the broad landscape. Below you is a green field of data, with patterns, trends, and irregularity. Machine learning is like having sharp eyesight, allowing you to spot patterns in that vast landscape. Instead of being told what to look for, it learns from the data, identifying patterns, making predictions, and evolving its understanding over time. Traditional machine learning uses algorithms to sift through this data, continuously learning and refining its predictions with each pass.

To add to our analogy, if traditional machine learning is like flying during the day, identifying familiar patterns, quantum machine learning can be seen as flying at night, with the capability to see subtle patterns hidden in the dim light, patterns that might be invisible during the day. Quantum computing, with its principles of superposition and entanglement, allows for the exploration of huge amounts of data simultaneously, tapping into patterns that have been elusive to classical computers.

Machine learning systems typically involve:

- **Data**: The landscape you are soaring over. This can be anything from images, texts, numbers, or more.

- **Model**: This is the type of "glasses" or "lenses" you wear to see the patterns. It's a mathematical structure that makes predictions based on data.

- **Training**: This involves "flying" repeatedly over the landscape (or going through the data multiple times) to refine the model's accuracy in its predictions.

Quantum computing brings a twist to these components. With the inherent ability of qubits, the "landscape" becomes richer and more dimensional. The "glasses" or models can see deeper connections, and the "flying" or training can potentially be exponentially faster, tapping into the quantum domain's advantages.

What are the motivations behind blending quantum computing and machine learning? We are creating a synergy that promises to redefine our understanding of data processing.

## Combining Quantum Computing and Machine Learning

Imagine for a moment that while soaring through the skies, you find areas where the winds are too strong, and flying with just your wings becomes difficult. Wouldn't it be valuable to have an additional propulsion system that could tap into the air currents and give you a powerful boost? This is the promise of combining quantum computing with machine learning.

## Tackling Complex Problems

There are problems in machine learning that are computationally intense for classical computers. Training large neural networks, finding patterns in massive datasets, or simulating complex systems can take a considerable amount of time and resources. Quantum computers can offer a computational speedup. Essentially, they can provide the 'boost' needed to address these challenges more timely.

## Harnessing Quantum

Quantum mechanics describes phenomena that don't resemble classical physics, such as superposition and entanglement. By integrating these principles into machine learning models, we can create algorithms that leverage the quantum domain's unique features. This isn't just about faster computations; it's about tapping into new ways of processing and understanding data.

## New Frontiers of Learning

It's time to upgrade our classical systems with Quantum systems that can represent and process information in new ways. For instance, they can explore multiple solutions to a problem thanks to superposition. This opens the door to novel machine learning techniques and algorithms, potentially leading to insights that were previously out of reach.

As we generate more and more data in today's digital age, scalability becomes a pressing concern. How do we process and derive meaningful insights from this ever-growing sea of data? Quantum computing offers potential solutions to scale up machine learning processes, ensuring we're not just collecting data but actually learning from it. Quantum computing represents the next frontier. Integrating it with machine learning now means being ahead of the curve and ready for the quantum age.

As we push the boundaries of classical computing, we're also approaching its limits. The next best move is combining quantum computing and machine learning, which is like outfitting a bird with jet engines. While the wings of classical machine learning allow for graceful glides and noteworthy maneuvers, the quantum boost can propel it to speeds and heights previously unimaginable. It's about harnessing the best of both worlds in data processing.

## Highlighting Benefits and Features of QML

As we continue soaring higher into the quantum skies, the panoramic view below presents many possibilities and wonders. Just as the bird's eye view provides insights unavailable from the ground, quantum machine learning offers advantages that are beyond the reach of classical machine learning. Let's unpack the treasures this high-altitude flight brings.

*Enhanced Computational Efficiency*

One of the standout promises of quantum computing is the potential for significant computational speedups. This means quicker training times for models and faster solutions to problems.

*Handling High-Dimensional Data*

Quantum systems can naturally represent high-dimensional vectors and patterns. In machine learning, where data can often be multi-dimensional (think of images, videos, or intricate datasets), quantum systems provide a natural playground, making processes like data classification or clustering more efficient. More on this later!

## Quantum Data Encoding

Quantum computers have a unique way of encoding data, tapping into quantum states. This encoding can capture more complex relationships in data, potentially leading to more accurate machine learning models. It's like having a supreme palette of colors to paint a picture, where nuances and details are more vividly depicted.

## Noise Resistance

Certain quantum algorithms display an inherent resistance to specific types of noise, making them robust in real-world, noisy environments. In the context of machine learning, this can lead to more resilient and reliable models.

## Quantum Parallelism

Quantum systems can explore multiple solutions concurrently, thanks to their ability to be in a superposition of states. This means that for specific problems, a quantum machine learning model can evaluate numerous potential outcomes at once, streamlining the decision-making process. The parallelism property is one of the key reasons why quantum computers might achieve supremacy, but that's another book.

## Enhanced Data Privacy

Quantum principles can be used to create protocols where data can be used in computations without revealing the actual data. This is immensely beneficial in sectors like healthcare, where data privacy is paramount, yet the insights from data are crucial.

## Tackling The Problems

With the union of quantum computing and machine learning, problems that were deemed too computationally intense or impossible for classical systems suddenly become possible. This opens the door to new discoveries and breakthroughs in various fields, from material science to finance.

We realize that the possibilities with quantum machine learning are limitless. The unique features and benefits it offers will reshape industries, drive innovation, and challenge our very understanding of data processing. Combining qubits and machine learning algorithms is more than a technological marvel; it's the dawn of a new era in computation. As we glide further into QML, we are not just spectators but active participants, ready to harness the winds of change.

## Quantum-Inspired Machine Learning Algorithms

*"When we talk about what a quantum-inspired algorithm is, we're speaking of its structure, behavior, and methodology rather than its physical appearance."*

-Pantheon Space Academy

Imagine, for a moment, that you're trying to mimic the flight of birds (true quantum algorithms) by using airplanes (classical algorithms). You observe how birds take advantage of air currents, how they glide, and how they flap their wings. Now, an airplane can't flap its wings. Still, engineers might design its wings to change shape or angle (a quantum-inspired approach) to gain some benefits birds have, without actually replicating proper bird flight.

In computing, "quantum-inspired" algorithms play a similar role. While not purely quantum, these algorithms are designed to imitate certain quantum processes, allowing them to be run on classical computers while still tapping into the advantages of quantum mechanics. They blend the familiar classical computing methods we've grown accustomed to with the aspirational processes only quantum mechanics can offer.

Why do we need this fusion? Pure quantum algorithms demand a full quantum computing environment to run. As of now, large-scale, error-free quantum computers are still on the horizon. However, the benefits of quantum mechanics, such as superposition and entanglement, are too tempting to wait for. That's where quantum-inspired algorithms come into play. They provide a way for researchers and developers to start applying some of the quantum advantages in our current classical computing platforms.

This middle-ground approach has given birth to many innovative algorithms, each offering unique solutions and abilities. As we soar further into this chapter, we'll look over some of the most well-known quantum-inspired machine learning algorithms, discover how they work, and witness their real-world applications. We have reached our cruising altitude and will now merge the known with the unknown.

## Dynamics of Machine Learning Algorithms

Imagine the algorithms as birds, each with their distinct way of soaring through the quantum skies. All birds share characteristics that enable them to fly – wings, feathers, and a lightweight skeleton. Similarly, most quantum machine learning algorithms share basic principles that grant them their quantum advantage.

At the heart of these algorithms lie qubits, the quantum equivalent of classical bits but with a twist. Unlike classical bits, which are either in a state of 0 or 1, qubits can exist in a superposition. In this state, they're both 0 and 1. This ability exponentially amplifies the amount of information a qubit can process.

Now, when multiple qubits are involved, they can become entangled, another trait of quantum mechanics. In an entangled state, the information of one qubit is dependent on another, no matter the distance between them. This interconnectedness allows

QUANTUM COMPUTING EXPLAINED FOR BEGINNERS

quantum algorithms to explore multiple solutions simultaneously, drastically reducing problem-solving time.

Having these core principles in mind sets the stage for understanding the nuances and specialties of each quantum machine learning algorithm. As we explore each one, remember the qubits' superposition and entanglement abilities as their wings and feathers, facilitating their flights through complex computational landscapes. What differentiates one algorithm from another is comparable to the different flight patterns and behaviors of distinct bird species.

With this foundational knowledge in place, let's begin to discover the unique traits and applications of the core quantum machine learning algorithms shaping our technological future.

## Quantum Support Vector Machines (QSVMs)

At the heart of machine learning, the primary goal is often to find patterns or make classifications. In classical systems, Support Vector Machines (SVMs) have been the go-to for this. They operate by finding a hyperplane, a boundary, that best separates the data into distinct classes. Now, enter the quantum realm, where Quantum Support Vector Machines (QSVMs) take flight.

*Distinct Quantum Touch*

Traditional SVMs scan through data linearly, one point at a time. QSVMs, however, leverage the power of quantum parallelism. This allows them to process vast swaths of data simultaneously. Moreover, QSVMs can utilize quantum gates, particularly those designed for phase estimation and amplitude amplification, to probe data points and find their relationships in fewer steps.

*Exploiting Quantum Features*

In a classical SVM, the feature space (a kind of landscape where data points are mapped based on their characteristics) can get quite complex, especially for intricate data sets. Quantum systems naturally live in high-dimensional spaces due to their superposition property. QSVMs exploit this, allowing for an elegant representation of complex feature spaces, which, in turn, simplifies the task of finding the optimal separating hyperplane.

*Applications & Strengths*

Where does the mastery of QSVMs truly shine? They are particularly suited for tasks where the data is high-dimensional, or the relationship between data points is non-linear. Think of complex fields like bioinformatics, where researchers grapple with massive genetic datasets, or financial markets, where the combination of numerous variables makes predictions notoriously challenging. QSVMs can cut through this complexity, offering insights that elude classical algorithms.

Quantum Support Vector Machines don't just "mimic" their classical counterparts; they elevate the game. By tapping into the properties of quantum mechanics, they offer a fresh approach to age-old classification problems, proving that the quantum skies have a lot of uncharted territory worth exploring.

## Quantum Neural Networks (QNNs)

One of the most exciting formations we encounter in our exploration of the quantum skies is the Quantum Neural Network (QNN). Just as birds form complex patterns in the sky, relying on each individual's movements and the overall flock's dynamics, neural networks—both classical and quantum—rely on intricate structures and interactions to process information.

*Unique Quantum Neurons*

At the core of any neural network are nodes or neurons. In QNNs, these neurons are the qubits. When these qubits interact, typically through quantum gates like the controlled-NOT gate or the Toffoli gate, they create a web of entangled states. This entanglement lets the quantum neurons "speak" to each other in a profoundly interconnected manner, which isn't possible classically.

*Training & Adaptation*

Training a neural network involves adjusting weights and biases to minimize errors. In QNNs, this process is amplified. Quantum parallelism allows QNNs to evaluate many possible configurations at once. Quantum Phase Estimation, a central algorithm in quantum computing, can also be employed to find the optimal weights with remarkable efficiency.

*Applications*

Quantum Neural Networks are incredibly potent when dealing with massive, intertwined datasets. Consider, for instance, the field of drug discovery. Here, molecules, with their infinite combinations of atoms and bonds, create complex structures. QNNs can simulate these molecular interactions at a depth that classical neural networks find challenging. Similarly, in areas like image recognition, where subtle patterns and details matter, QNNs can bring refinement to what classical methods miss.

It's clear that Quantum Neural Networks are not just a superficial translation of their classical counterparts into the quantum domain. They are a reimagining, leveraging the unique strengths of quantum mechanics to process information in novel, more profound ways. As we soar through the quantum expanse, viewing the beauty of QNNs, with their intricate patterns and deep connections, is a testament to the potential that awaits us in the quantum age.

## Quantum Clustering

As we continue our flight, a new pattern emerges below, reminding me of the way birds gather at watering holes or form colonies. These gatherings aren't random; they have an order and rhythm to them. Similarly, clustering or grouping similar data points together is a pivotal task in the world of data. Quantum clustering is a shining example of how quantum principles can be harnessed to execute this task with unprecedented finesse.

*Quantum Distance Metrics*

At the heart of clustering lies the concept of distance. How far or close are data points from one another? Quantum clustering introduces a new perspective on this. Instead of classical distances, it employs quantum states' overlaps. We utilize quantum interference patterns to determine closeness. This allows for capturing subtleties in data relationships that might be missed in classical contexts.

## Quantum Amplitude Amplification

One of the star players in quantum clustering is Quantum Amplitude Amplification. This technique bolsters the probability of finding a sought-after quantum state. In the context of clustering, it aids in honing in on clusters efficiently, making the process faster and more accurate.

## Applications

The beauty of quantum clustering lies in its adaptability. It is especially suited for high-dimensional data, where classical methods fall short due to the 'curse of dimensionality.' Consider genomics, where data points (genes or gene sequences) reside in high-dimensional spaces. Quantum clustering can identify patterns and groupings in such data more effectively. Another area of promise is finance, where stock behaviors or trading patterns across global markets can be clustered to show insights that remain obscured in purely classical analysis.

In the grand spectacle of our quantum flight, quantum clustering shines as an ideal of precision and depth. By reinterpreting the fundamental ideas of closeness and groupings through a quantum lens, it offers a fresh viewpoint, allowing us to discern patterns and connections that were once hidden in plain sight.

## Advanced Quantum Algorithms

The beauty of exploration lies in the ever-present potential, always promising new areas to discover. As we journeyed through the quantum skies, we've encountered some algorithms that blend quantum mechanics with machine learning. However, like seasoned explorers hungry for more profound adventures, we now turn our attention to the more intricate algorithms that lie ahead.

Advanced quantum algorithms, often drawing inspiration from multiple disciplines and quantum principles, represent the frontier of quantum machine learning. Unlike the algorithms we've touched upon before, which primarily brought quantum benefits to traditional ML models, these advanced algorithms go a step further. They redefine the foundational processes of machine learning from a quantum mindset, making them uniquely tailored for the quantum domain. Think of them as specially crafted aircraft, designed not just for regular flight but for complex aerobatic maneuvers, extreme altitudes, and challenging atmospheric conditions.

But why this added complexity? The world of data, in its vastness, presents challenges that often push classical algorithms to their limits. These advanced quantum algorithms, born out of extensive research and innovation, are designed to tackle such complexities head-on, offering solutions that were once out of reach. Their design, sophistication, and methodologies make them stand out, capable of reshaping our understanding of data and prediction.

As we navigate through these advanced algorithms, keep your aviator goggles on. We're about to experience some high-altitude quantum aerobatics that promise to change our perspective on machine learning's potential!

## Flying High on High-Dimensional Data

As we search the vast quantum skies, we encounter intriguing cloud formations. Some are wispy and scattered, while others are dense and multi-layered. In the world of data, these "clouds" are comparable to the different dimensions or layers of information we handle. Quantum Kernel Methods (QKMs) are the advanced navigation tools that help us easily and precisely maneuver through these stunning data clouds.

### The Foundation of QKMs

At its heart, a kernel method is a machine learning technique to transform data to be more easily processed and understood. Think of it as adjusting the scope from which you view a cloud formation, making it simpler to discern its structure. In classical machine learning, kernel methods take non-linearly separable data and transform it into a higher dimension where it becomes linearly separable, like finding the right angle to view our cloud.

But quantum kernels? They introduce an entirely new level of transformation. By employing the principles of quantum mechanics, QKMs can handle high-dimensional data much more efficiently than their classical counterparts. They leverage the power of superposition and entanglement to process information in ways that classical systems simply can't.

*Distinguishing QKMs from Classical Methods*

While classical kernel methods rely on mathematical functions to perform these transformations, QKMs use quantum gates and operations. By doing so, they can represent and process enormous amounts of high-dimensional data on qubits. This doesn't just mean they're faster; it means they can handle types of data and complexities that are out of reach for classical methods.

Another standout feature? Their resilience. Even when faced with noise—an inherent challenge in today's quantum processors—QKMs maintain their edge. They're designed to function during turbulence, continuing to process high-dimensional data seamlessly.

*Practical Significance of QKMs*

So, why does all of this matter? As our world becomes more data-driven, the complexity and depth of the data we handle grows. The applications are endless, whether it's analyzing genetic information, predicting climate changes, or understanding financial markets. QKMs offer a way to process this data efficiently and accurately. For instance, in the medical field, QKMs are being explored for their potential to analyze genetic data to identify disease markers, providing insights that were previously out of our reach.

*Quantum Flight with QKMs*

In our quantum journey, QKMs are like the advanced navigational systems that allow us to explore cloud formations that were previously untouchable. As we make progress in the quantum domain, these methods will continue to be invaluable tools, helping us unlock the mysteries of the data landscape and ensuring our flight through the quantum skies is enlightening and impactful.

## A Grand Unification, QSVT

In our exploration, we've witnessed quantum mechanics and machine learning come together harmoniously, each elevating the other to new heights. Yet, as we continue to soar, specific moments and techniques stand out like dazzling constellations in the expanse of the night sky. One such stellar phenomenon is the Quantum Singular Value Transformation (QSVT).

The kingdom of quantum computing is vast, but QSVT holds a special place, like a pilot steering us toward more efficient data processing in machine learning. At its core, QSVT is a quantum algorithm, a beneficiary to classical singular value techniques, which have been used to decode complex datasets by breaking them down into simpler, digestible components.

The foundational principle of QSVT is rooted deeply in quantum mechanics. It uses both superposition and entanglement to perform computations in ways that classical computers can only dream of. QSVT leverages quantum states' raw, unharnessed power to process information, transform it, and derive value from it with unprecedented precision.

Delving deeper into its mechanics, QSVT often involves specific quantum gates and circuits that aid these transformative processes. While classical singular value techniques rely on linear algebra and matrix decompositions to find patterns in data, QSVT employs quantum gates that can perform these tasks at exponentially faster rates. This speed comes with an added layer of depth in understanding the data, thanks to the probabilistic nature of quantum mechanics.

What makes QSVT truly remarkable, though, is its adaptability. It's like the agile jet in our flight analogy, capable of intricate maneuvers that big commercial planes can't achieve. QSVT excels in handling dense, multi-dimensional data, unraveling its complexities in ways that classical methods fall short of. This capability becomes a blessing, especially when working with massive datasets that have hidden patterns waiting to be uncovered.

As we talk about real-world scenarios, QSVT has shown immense promise in areas ranging from finance, where understanding data patterns can predict market movements, to healthcare, where analyzing complex biological data can lead to groundbreaking medical discoveries. The flexibility and precision of QSVT make it a frontrunner in the race toward quantum dominance in machine learning.

In the future skies of quantum machine learning, QSVT shines brightly, reminding us of the untapped potential that awaits. Just as pilots rely on constellations for navigation, QSVT serves as a guide, pointing towards a tomorrow where quantum processes and machine learning unite to redefine what's possible. As we continue our flight, with QSVT illuminating our path, the horizon seems filled with endless possibilities, each more exciting than the last.

## TensorFlow Quantum

*Bridging Quantum and Classical World*

In the computing cosmos, a beacon of hope and innovation arises: TensorFlow Quantum. Originating from Google, this remarkable platform was designed in collaboration with the quantum computing company, X, and is tailored explicitly for the rapidly growing field of quantum machine learning. At its heart, TensorFlow Quantum is more than just another computational tool; it's the connective tissue that fuses the unbounded potential of quantum computing with the established skills of classical machine learning.

Imagine our quantum analogy of flying through the skies, navigating through clouds of complicated algorithms and data landscapes. In such an adventure, TensorFlow Quantum is our cockpit control system, expertly guiding our flight through familiar terrains and uncharted quantum domains. While quantum computing offers the raw power of qubits, superposition, and entanglement, classical systems present a well-established infrastructure, giant data sets, and matured algorithms. TensorFlow Quantum brilliantly bridges these worlds, ensuring a harmonious coexistence.

What truly sets TensorFlow Quantum apart is its unique features tailored for quantum complexity. This platform provides a holistic environment where quantum datasets, quantum models, and classical neural networks interact seamlessly. It uses the quantum phenomena to optimize machine learning tasks, delivering results that classical systems would find respectable, especially when dealing with quantum-specific challenges.

In the ever-evolving landscape of research and development, TensorFlow Quantum has carved a niche for itself. It's a tool and a leader for collaborations, fostering partnerships between tech giants, academic researchers, and quantum startups. These synergies have birthed studies and breakthroughs, accelerating our understanding and application of quantum machine learning.

In the grand narrative of our quantum quest, TensorFlow Quantum emerges as an essential co-pilot. It doesn't just help us soar; it ensures we fly with precision, power, and purpose. As we continue our journey, with the horizon filled with promises of quantum breakthroughs, TensorFlow Quantum helps us navigate these skies with unmatched elegance.

## Comparative Advantages of Quantum Algorithms

Quantum mechanics offers a unique perspective, an advantage not just of altitude but of possibilities. Similarly, quantum-inspired machine learning algorithms present capabilities that transcend those of classical systems. As we gaze down from our lofty quantum viewpoint, it becomes clear why these quantum algorithms are the rising stars in the computational cosmos.

### High-Dimensional Data Handling

In our journey, consider each data point as a star. In classical computing, the more stars (or data points), the more challenging the navigation. Quantum algorithms, however, thrive in such high-dimensional spaces. Thanks to the principle of superposition, qubits can digest large amounts of information simultaneously. This ability is like seeing multiple flight paths at once and choosing the best one in real time.

*Enhanced Processing*

If superposition is about possibilities, entanglement is about connections. Imagine two aircraft communicating instantaneously, regardless of the distance between them. This quantum sensation allows quantum algorithms to process interconnected data more intuitively than classical algorithms that view data points in isolation.

*Optimized Solutions*

We continue our flight analogy; interference can be likened to a plane's aerodynamic adjustments to avoid turbulent air and find smoother pathways. Quantum algorithms use interference to sift through and eliminate incorrect solutions, focusing only on the optimal ones, making them experts at solving complex optimization problems.

*Scalability and Future Readiness*

While today's quantum computers are in their infancy, quantum algorithms are already designed for scalability. As quantum hardware evolves, these algorithms will smoothly integrate, harnessing greater power and solving even more complex problems. It's like creating an aircraft today that's ready to navigate the more advanced air traffic systems of tomorrow.

*Natural Compatibility with Quantum Mechanics*

Some tasks inherently possess quantum properties, like simulating quantum systems in pharmaceutical research or material science. Quantum algorithms are naturally suited for these tasks, eliminating the need for approximations that classical algorithms often resort to.

*Exponential Speedups for Specific Problems*

Certain problems that would take classical computers ages to solve can be addressed in mere seconds with quantum algorithms. This dramatic speed advantage isn't universal but applies to specific problems, offering breakthrough possibilities in cryptography, optimization, and simulations.

In the broad geography of computation, while classical algorithms have paved the way, quantum algorithms promise uncharted territories and heights yet to be explored. As we soar with quantum machine learning, these advantages form the powerful tailwinds, propelling us faster and farther into the future of computation.

# Navigating Quantum Patents

*The Emerging Economy of QML*

In our voyage through the vast quantum skies, patents shine brightly, much like guiding stars illuminating our path. Picture this: seasoned aviators steering their aircraft, not just by instruments but also by the constellations stretching endlessly above. In quantum machine learning, these patents offer the same kind of guidance, the reassurance of a well-lit path in an otherwise overwhelming sky.

In the constantly evolving economy of technology, quantum machine learning promises to deliver massive innovations. This growing field has given rise to a distinct economic market, indicated by a surge in patents tailored to quantum machine learning technologies. These aren't just tiresome paperwork; each patent represents a step forward, a novel idea that promises to reshape industries and redefine what's achievable. From the new algorithms designed for modern warfare's cybersecurity applications to the sophisticated encryption schemes strengthening financial transactions, these patents underline the merger of quantum mechanics and computational intelligence.

Furthermore, one must recognize these patents' transformative potential in the medical world, particularly in drug discovery. The ability to model chemical interactions at a quantum level opens doors to unique precision, promising treatments, and medicines that are both effective and personalized. Yet, what truly underscores the magnitude of this patent-driven revolution is its trajectory. When one observes the issued patents, the exponential growth of the quantum machine learning patent market distinctly mirrors that of the broader machine learning hype from its early days. This parallel hints at the dominant role quantum technologies are poised to play in the coming years. This signals an upcoming shift in the way we harness computational power.

How do you navigate the patents? A field as cutting-edge as quantum machine learning demands a functional approach. When sifting through the sea of information, it's essential to have a method to identify innovation. For this exploration, a sweeping data collection was conducted using the United States Patent and Trademark Office (USPTO) database, a comprehensive resource for searching patents. I focused on select terms at the heart of quantum machine learning: "Quantum AND Machine Learning", "Quantum AND Markov", "Quantum AND Boltzmann", and "Quantum AND Neural Networks." By targeting these specific intersections, the intent was to cast a wide net that captures quantum innovations in reinforcement learning, deep learning, and their advanced combinations.

The findings from this targeted search offer an enlightening snapshot of the quantum machine learning economy. Not only do they reveal the sheer volume and diversity of patents in the arena, but they also emphasize the rapid pace of innovation. Each term, representing a distinct aspect of quantum computing or machine learning, shows how researchers and innovators are pushing the boundaries, seeking to merge quantum principles with our modern world in unprecedented ways. The patents that emerged hint at applications and solutions set to transform industries across the board.

## Patent Success in QML

From the many quantum innovations, one particular company, Zapata Computing, streaks across the sky with a trail of patents, showcasing the real-world implications of quantum machine learning. One of their groundbreaking patents pertains to the Variational Quantum Factoring (VQF) and Quantum-Assisted Defense Against Adversarial AI (QDAI) algorithms. While these technical titles might seem obscure, their implications in our digital world are both profound and transformative.

Zapata's QDAI algorithm is a sentinel against hostile attacks on Machine Learning (ML) models. For those soaring in the digital domain, adversarial attacks are like unpredictable air pockets that can disrupt a flight's stability. They introduce tiny yet intentionally crafted variations to data, confusing machine learning classifiers and leading them astray. As if navigating this turbulence wasn't challenging enough, quantum computers introduce another layer of complexity, giving a unique quantum noise that further misguides these models. But here's where Zapata's brilliance shines. Their patented QDAI is trained to recognize and counter these quantum noises, acting like a pilot skillfully steering clear of turbulence, ensuring that ML models deliver accurate results even in the face of these quantum disruptions.

Beyond just the security implications, this technology highlights the enormous potential of QML. As cyber threats evolve, the ability to use quantum mechanics to bolster our defense mechanisms becomes priceless. It's not just about protecting data but certifying that the very algorithms we trust to process and interpret it remain uncompromised. With innovations like those from Zapata Computing, our journey through the quantum skies becomes thrilling and secure, holding promise for a future where quantum and classical harmoniously coexist.

The quantum horizon continues to glow with promise, and as we steer from the achievements of Zapata Computing, another star in our quantum sky emerges: D-Wave Systems. With over two decades dedicated to pioneering quantum computing technologies, D-Wave has established itself as a key player in the quantum domain. Their trajectory in the quantum sky has been nothing short of meteoric, and they've marked their territory with an array of patents and groundbreaking innovations.

D-Wave's collaboration with industrial titans such as Volkswagen and NASA exemplifies their commitment to practical quantum solutions. Imagine a quantum navigator that can find the most efficient route within the chaotic traffic of data – that's the sort of optimization problems D-Wave's technologies tackle. Their quantum solutions offer a distinct advantage, carving pathways through computational challenges where classical systems would find themselves deprived.

Moreover, D-Wave's endeavors continue beyond optimizing existing processes. They've ventured into designing specialized chips tailored for machine learning tasks. These chips act like powerful engines in the infinite data clouds we navigate, applying the raw quantum energy to process and understand data at speeds and depths previously viewed as untouchable.

Through partnerships, inventions, and consistent innovation, D-Wave Systems ensures our quantum aspirations aren't just about understanding the skies but also about leveraging their vast potential. They exemplify the very essence of quantum machine learning, demonstrating that the fusion of quantum mechanics and computational intelligence is not just theoretical but practical and transformative.

Let's fly from the impressive achievements of D-Wave Systems to the luminous trail of BTQ Technologies Inc., another trailblazer making its mark in the quantum domain. As I sorted through hundreds of quantum innovations, BTQ emerged as a sentinel, safeguarding the digital expanse.

With data breaches becoming increasingly prevalent and the looming shadow of quantum computers threatening to break traditional cryptographic methods, the need for unbreakable encryption has never been greater. Enter BTQ and their game-changing, patented quantum-safe encryption technology. Just as pilots need foolproof navigational tools to traverse challenging weather conditions, industries ranging from finance to healthcare desperately require unbreachable security measures to transmit sensitive data safely.

BTQ's innovation is not just about encryption but a holistic data security approach. The patented process involves generating private cryptographic keys from a shared random vector, ensuring maximum privacy in data transmission. I'm impressed by the versatility of their invention to adapt to various mathematical functions, ensuring it remains resilient against potential breaches. They've created a strong barrier called a cryptogram, where confidential data is compressed and combined with random data. It perfectly blends data and randomness, ensuring a robust and unyielding security layer.

This encryption method is like having a quantum cape, making sensitive data indistinguishable from the randomness, thwarting any potential meddlers in their tracks. As Olivier Roussy Newton, the

CEO of BTQ, sharply puts it, their patented technology is more than just a cryptographic method; it's a revolution in data security. As the quantum domain grows, with companies like BTQ leading the way, the digital future looks promising and secure.

## Advantages and Challenges of Quantum Machine Learning

*"The best way to predict the future is to invent it."*

- Alan Kay

As we soar higher into the quantum skies, the expansive view below reveals the vivid patterns of data stretching out like cloud formations. These patterns, reminiscent of the datasets we encounter in computational landscapes, often pose challenges for classical machines, but for our quantum systems, they signify newfound pockets of potential.

## Improved Computational Efficiency

Merging the power of quantum mechanics and quantum machine learning (QML) brings a transformative change in computational efficiency. Where classical computers laboriously sift through data, quantum computers process information in parallel with their superposition and entanglement. Imagine flying through a dense cloud cover, where each cloud represents a data point. A classical approach would entail navigating each cloud one by one. In contrast, a quantum system, much like a bird's panoramic view, would instantly perceive and understand the entire formation.

~ 276 ~

## Big Data Analytics

Our digital age is marked by the proliferation of data. Every aspect of our lives generates data, from social media interactions to financial transactions and scientific experiments. This surge in data, often termed 'Big Data', poses challenges for classical analytics tools, which can get overwhelmed by the absolute volume and complexity. Enter quantum computing. Its inherent parallelism and capacity to represent huge amounts of information on individual qubits grant it a distinct advantage. Like a high-tech radar system, quantum analytics can swiftly scan, interpret, and draw patterns from these immense data landscapes. Whether it's predicting stock market trends from millions of transactions or decoding human genome sequences, quantum's edge is undeniable. In our quantum journey, the sky is not the limit; it's just the beginning.

As we continue our flight, it's crucial to appreciate these capabilities, for they set the stage for the quantum optimism in machine learning. But like any journey, challenges await; understanding them is as essential as recognizing the advantages. Our next phase goes into the specific quantum techniques that are shaping this digital world.

## Simplifying Complex Data

Imagine standing at the edge of an intricate maze, looking at countless paths, each representing a piece of data. Traditionally, navigating this maze to find relationships between data points would be a monumental challenge. Enter vector embeddings, the unsung heroes of the machine learning world. At their core, vector embeddings are mathematical tools that transform high-dimensional data—like our vast maze—into more manageable, lower-dimensional representations. Think of it as viewing the maze from above, gaining a clearer perspective of the paths and their relationships.

My excitement for vector embeddings, especially in the quantum domain, is hardly containable. The reason? BIG data. We live in an era where data is exploding. Each day, quintillions of bytes of data are generated. While we've made strides with classical embeddings, there are still inefficiencies. Quantum-enhanced embeddings promise not just improvements but extreme changes.

Looking into the technical heart of vector embeddings, traditionally, they've been used in machine learning to capture the essence of data points in lower-dimensional spaces without losing much information. For instance, in natural language processing, words are transformed into vectors so that words with similar meanings are close in this vector space. This closeness is not about the words but their context, semantics, and intricate relationships.

Now, sprinkle a bit of quantum magic onto this. Quantum-enhanced vector embeddings can leverage the principles of superposition and entanglement. While classical embeddings might represent data in, let's say, 300 dimensions, quantum embeddings can represent the same data more compactly, but with more detail. The state of a qubit provides a unique advantage in capturing complex data structures.

Moreover, when I talk about BIG data, I'm referring to datasets so vast that classical computers struggle to process them efficiently. With quantum embeddings, the potential to analyze and interpret this data is amplified, not just by handling more data, but by understanding it at a deeper, more interconnected level.

In the grand narrative of quantum machine learning, vector embeddings might not always take center stage or receive any attention. Still, their role is similar to the backstage crew in a play—making sure everything runs seamlessly. As we move into the quantum era, it's tools like these that will drive efficiency, precision, and depth in our understanding of the data landscapes we navigate.

## A Stepping Stone for Advanced Quantum Computation

At its core, a quantum walk is a quantum analog of the classical random walk. However, while classical random walks are fundamentally random processes, quantum walks are driven by deterministic unitary evolution, enabling them to harness quantum interference effects.

Quantum walks can be categorized into discrete-time and continuous-time walks. In discrete-time quantum walks, a "coin operation" decides the direction of the walk, followed by a conditional shift operation based on the coin's state. Continuous-time quantum walks, on the other hand, don't rely on a coin; instead, they evolve directly on the underlying graph or structure via the Hamiltonian of the system.

From a computational perspective, quantum walks are groundbreaking because they can process information in ways classical algorithms can't. The interference patterns inherent to quantum walks allow for faster solutions to classically hard problems, like the element distinctness problem or searching in structured databases.

A notable attribute of quantum walks is their capacity for universal quantum computation without time-dependent control. This means that by setting up the right initial conditions and letting the system evolve, the quantum walk can simulate any quantum operation, making it a dynamic tool in the toolbox of quantum algorithm designers.

In practical applications, this allows quantum computers to perform complex computations with fewer resources and less intervention, making quantum walks an interesting quantum phenomenon and a pivotal technique that propels the quantum computing field further.

## Mastering the Quantum Data Flow

In our quantum journey, imagine data as our primary cargo, with some items (data) designed for the quantum skies, while others belong to the classical realm. Just as specific tools ensure that the cargo is suitable for various phases of flight, in the quantum computing world, these tools are embodied by TensorFlow Quantum, quantization, and dequantization.

## *TensorFlow Quantum*

This is the main control panel in our aircraft, ensuring everything runs smoothly. Developed by Google in collaboration with quantum experts, it's an open-source tool that allows classical neural networks and quantum circuits to interact seamlessly. If our flight involves hopping between classical and quantum skies, TensorFlow Quantum ensures we do so without turbulence.

## *Quantization*

Before taking off into the quantum realm, we need to make sure our classical data (or cargo) is properly packaged or encoded for quantum processing. Quantization is this packaging process. It converts classical data into a format (quantum states) suitable for quantum circuits. Think of it as adjusting the weight and size of cargo to guarantee it fits perfectly in our quantum aircraft.

## *Dequantization*

Once our quantum flight concludes and we need to land back in the classical world, our quantum-formatted data has to be translated back into a format that classical computers understand. Dequantization is this translation process, converting quantum results back into classical data. It's like unpacking and preparing our cargo for its next destination in the classical realm.

Both quantization and dequantization processes have intricacies, depending on the nature of the data and the specific quantum operations applied. They play a critical role in providing an efficient transition between classical and quantum domains, with minimal data loss. By mastering TensorFlow Quantum and the processes of quantization and dequantization, we establish that our leaps between the classical and quantum skies are smooth and optimized for the best results.

## Navigating Through Quantum Turbulence

As we soar through the quantum skies, it's not always smooth sailing. Just as pilots must encounter atmospheric disturbances, we must address the challenges of Quantum Machine Learning (QML).

*Qubit Noise, Error Correction, and Decoherence*

Remember the delicate balance required in quantum physics and architecture? In QML, this balance is just as pressing. Qubit noise refers to the unforeseen disturbances that might affect our quantum data. Think of it as gusts of wind that can throw our plane slightly off course. While qubits have the power to process information in ways classical bits can't, they are sensitive and can be influenced by their surroundings.

Decoherence, meanwhile, is like the fading strength of a radio signal over a long flight. Over time, qubits can lose their quantum properties if not properly maintained. Just as pilots use instruments to counteract the effects of turbulence and maintain a plane's altitude, in QML, we use error correction techniques to make sure our quantum data remains accurate, even in the face of these disturbances.

## Large-Scale Quantum Computers

Similar to the first-generation aircraft, current quantum computers are remarkable engineering feats but have limitations. They're still smaller than we'd like and error-prone for some complex machine learning tasks. We're still in the early days, refining our technology and verifying that our quantum planes can handle longer, more intricate expeditions.

## Trade-offs and Comparisons

Every choice in aviation comes with a trade-off. The same holds for QML. While quantum algorithms can handle tasks that classical ones find impossible, they require specialized hardware and are still being refined. Classical machine learning, like well-established commercial airlines, is mature, with infrastructure and years of optimization. On the other hand, Quantum machine learning is like an emerging breed of aircraft – faster and more powerful, but still being tested for all terrains and weather conditions. Weighing QML against its classical counterpart is about understanding when to deploy each for maximum efficiency and impact.

## Learning From Mistakes

It's essential to acknowledge and navigate these challenges. Recognizing them allows us to innovate and refine, assisting in our continued progress in the skies of Quantum Machine Learning.

# Looking Forward

*Charting New Territories in the Quantum Skies*

As we reach the concluding leg of our journey through the chapter, it's great to understand where we currently soar and anticipate the horizons waiting to be explored. The present landscape of quantum machine learning is like dawn breaking over an expansive sky, casting the first light on regions with potential.

The **current state** of QML is marked by an energetic blend of academics, industry innovations, and a global community of researchers passionately pushing boundaries. Pilot programs, early-stage quantum computers, and budding algorithms are like the initial test flights—each one providing impressive data, refining our approach, and ensuring the skies are safer and more efficient for following journeys. Collaborations between tech giants, quantum startups, and academic institutions fuel this momentum, fostering an ecosystem of rapid learning and adaptation.

With advancements in quantum hardware and deeper insights into quantum algorithms, we're on the brink of a digital shift that some have labeled as The Fourth Revolution. The coming decade promises QML models that can decode the most intricate patterns, from climate modeling to space exploration. As quantum computing power strengthens, we can anticipate breakthroughs that were the stuff of science fiction just a few years ago. Imagine machine learning models that can predict and understand climate changes with unprecedented accuracy, or healthcare algorithms that can model and analyze every single molecular interaction in real-time, potentially unlocking cures for the world's most challenging ailments.

Before we close the cabin doors on this chapter, let's make a pit stop back at Machine Learning (ML) Central. Think of it like that end-of-trip luggage check – 'Did I pack my socks? My charger? My understanding of ML?' It's more than just algorithms and computations; it's the unsung hero of the digital empire. Final call for **Machine Learning (ML) in simple terms:**

- **Definition:** A subset of AI. It's a method of data analysis that automates analytical model building. ML allows computers to learn from data without being explicitly programmed for that task.

- **Scope**: Specifically deals with the development of algorithms that can learn from and make predictions or decisions based on data.

- **Goal**: The primary purpose is to enable machines to learn from data so that they can give accurate predictions and decisions.

- **Learning**: ML learns from data; hence, it adjusts its predictions and decisions as it receives more data.

- **Types**: Can be categorized based on how learning is achieved, such as supervised learning, unsupervised learning, and reinforcement learning.

While this chapter concludes, the quantum quest is far from over. As we segue into considerations of ethics in our upcoming explorations, it's paramount to approach the future of QML with a blend of optimism, responsibility, and a relentless search for knowledge. The quantum future is filled with potential and promise, and the path ahead will be as stimulating as the chapters we've traversed together.

# CHAPTER 9

## ETHICS AND SOCIAL IMPLICATIONS

*"Ethics is knowing the difference between what you have a right to do and what is right to do."*

– Potter Stewart

In the rapidly evolving world of quantum computing, this profound statement by Justice Stewart resonates more than ever. As we stand at the dawn of a new technological era, this chapter discusses the ethical maze surrounding quantum advancements.

The brilliance of quantum's potential is matched only by the weight of responsibility it brings. Pioneering this frontier, I often grapple with questions that extend beyond physical technology. Who truly bears the mantle of moral and ethical stewardship? Is it the relentless scientists pushing the boundaries of what we know? The corporations, with their vast resources and influential reach? The governments entrusted with the welfare of its citizens? Or is it us, the collective society, the end-users and beneficiaries of this futuristic technology?

The fabric of responsibility is entangled among all these entities, creating a complex puzzle that's challenging to solve. Having navigated the intricate corridors of technology, business, and policy,

I've realized that a singular, definitive answer still needs to be reached. However, one conviction stands unwavering: Ethical considerations are not mere add-ons to the quantum narrative. They are its very soul, our "why", guiding its evolution at every step.

While I stand firmly as a Quantum Computing-AI optimist, boundless potential should be paired with thoughtful reflection. I encourage you, not to blindly share in my enthusiasm but to bring your own critical thought and inquiry to the table. As we navigate this groundbreaking era, it's essential that we ask questions, demand responsibility, and participate actively in the blending of this technology with our lives. Let's venture on this exploration together, making room for wonder, analysis, and the ethical considerations that will guide the next wave of innovation.

## Ethical Implications of Quantum Computing

*Quantum Computing and Cryptography*

In today's digital age, the security of our online data is paramount. Everything from our emails to our bank details and medical records is protected using cryptography. It's like an intricate digital lock and key system, where data is locked away, and only the correct key can unlock and access it.

Traditional computers, even the fastest ones we have today, would need thousands of years to try out all the possible keys and crack the encryption. But here's the catch: Quantum computers, with their incredible processing power, might one day be able to do this in a matter of hours or even minutes.

# The Balance

*User Privacy vs. National Security*

A leading quantum physicist, Dr. Alicia Cortez, once remarked, "The same quantum technology that promises medical breakthroughs and ultra-efficient logistical solutions also has the power to undermine the very fabric of online security."

On one hand, quantum computing poses a potential threat to individual privacy. If malicious actors get access to quantum capabilities before protective measures are in place, everything we thought was secure online could be at risk.

Yet, on the other side of the debate stands national security. Governments argue that quantum capabilities could be a crucial tool in fighting crime, terrorism, and other threats. The ability to decrypt communications quickly could, in some cases, mean the difference between life and death.

We must recognize that the debate isn't black and white. Here are a few thought-starters:

- How do we strike a balance between individual privacy rights and collective security needs?

- Are there ethical considerations in potentially creating quantum-proof encryptions, making it impossible for governments to access data even when it's deemed necessary?

- What mechanisms and checks should be in place to prevent misuse, and who gets to decide?

The world of quantum computing is as much about these critical philosophical and ethical questions as it is about the technology itself. The choices we make in navigating these challenges will shape the digital landscape of our quantum future.

As we give thought to quantum computing and cryptography, it becomes apparent that the reach of this technology stretches far beyond just securing our emails. The broader implications of quantum computing will impact privacy, ownership, security, and fairness.

In an age where data has often been dubbed the "new oil," the right to personal data **privacy** becomes paramount. Quantum computing could break today's cryptographic standards, making what was once private suddenly very public. The question arises: How do we ensure that the quantum tools that promise to improve our lives in so many ways don't simultaneously strip away our right to privacy?

**Ownership** in the quantum realm is complicated. At a superficial level, who owns quantum technology? Is it large tech corporations, academia, or governments? And as these entities gain the power to access exceptional amounts of data, how do we draw the boundaries of digital ownership? More philosophically, if quantum computing can simulate complex drug interactions or design new materials, who owns these findings and the subsequent real-world applications?

While the cryptographic concerns form the tip of the **security** iceberg, there's much more lurking beneath the surface. Quantum computers could boost the field of cybersecurity, both strengthening defenses and empowering attackers. The arms race between hackers and protectors could escalate to unforeseen levels, making our navigation of the digital realm a constantly evolving challenge.

The start of any trailblazing technology invariably begs the question: Who has access? If quantum computing remains in the hands of a select few—nations or corporations—it could lead to vast power imbalances. The digital divide could widen, with those harnessing quantum capabilities having a significant advantage over those who don't. **Fairness**, in this context, encompasses not just access to the technology but also the benefits it brings and the potential consequences of its misuse.

As quantum technology matures, we find ourselves at an inflection point. Dr. Sameer Rao, a tech ethicist, puts it succinctly: "Quantum computing isn't just about faster processing speeds or groundbreaking algorithms. It's a mirror reflecting our societal values, aspirations, and fears. In this mirror, we must see not just the promise but also the responsibility."

In our rapidly digitizing world, trust is paramount. Quantum computing stands at the nexus of this trust, poised with the power to process vast swathes of information. However, it's crucial to remember that quantum computers only know and interpret the data they're fed; they're not conscious entities discerning truth from falsehood on their own.

This brings us to a pressing moral dilemma: In a world armed with quantum capabilities, who becomes the arbiter of truth? Entrusting this immense responsibility to a centralized authority can be dangerous. History teaches us that such power, when unchecked, can suppress legitimate voices, disguising censorship as a fight against "fake news". Yet, a passive approach might leave us vulnerable to amplified disinformation campaigns, further straining the bonds of societal trust.

The optimal path forward lies in championing transparency, decentralization, and open-source principles. By distributing the power of truth verification and ensuring that quantum systems' inner workings remain accessible to all, we can encourage an environment where trust is built collaboratively, not dictated from above. In this quantum-augmented future, the question isn't just who should steer our collective narrative, but how we all can play a part in ensuring its integrity.

Our exploration of the quantum domain is just beginning, and these ethical concerns will shape its trajectory. Engaging with them proactively, rather than reactively, could be the difference between a quantum future that empowers humanity and one that challenges the very essence of a just society.

## Ethical Risks

*Treading with Caution in a Quantum Future*

While the possibilities of quantum computing seem limitless, it's mindful to address the ethical challenges that emerge in its wake. The world is on the threshold of a quantum leap, and with every leap comes the risk of a stumble. Next are only a few concerns that experts, including insights from Deloitte, have raised regarding the rapid climb of quantum technologies.

*Job Displacement*

Quantum computers, with their unmatched problem-solving ability, promise efficiency levels currently unseen in modern computing. This capability isn't merely about crunching numbers faster but potentially rendering whole professions and industries redundant. Financial modeling, complex simulations, intricate design work – fields that currently need significant manpower might soon be within the control of a quantum machine working in mere seconds. What becomes of the workforce in such scenarios? The displacement isn't just a question of jobs but of identity and purpose for countless individuals.

*Corporate Monopolization*

A pressing concern echoed by many is the possible monopolization of quantum technologies by a select few corporations. With significant entry barriers in terms of cost and expertise, quantum computing could become a playground for the elite, resulting in the centralization of power and influence. This concentration could restrain innovation, creating barriers for startups and researchers who have groundbreaking ideas but need more resources to bring them to market.

*Uneven Global Advancement*

The global landscape is dotted with disparities, and quantum computing could make them worse. Developed nations and tech hubs, with their financial might and technical know-how, might leap ahead, leaving others in the quantum dust. This isn't merely about economic supremacy but about disproportionately influencing global policies, regulations, and norms surrounding quantum technology.

*Misuse and Malintent*

With great power comes great responsibility, and quantum computing is no exception. In the hands of malicious actors, be it individuals, corporations, or nations, quantum capabilities could be weaponized, leading to unforeseen threats. The ethical dilemma here extends to developers and regulators: How do we ensure responsible development and deployment of quantum technologies?

Drawing from Deloitte's analysis, it becomes evident that the promise of quantum computing is linked with ethical challenges. Their report underscores a sentiment echoed by many in the tech community: it's not just about what quantum computing *can* do, but what it *should* do.

Navigating the quantum future will require a spectrum of voices – policymakers, ethicists, technologists, and the general public – to weave together a narrative that celebrates innovation while ensuring it doesn't come at the cost of our societal values and shared humanity.

*Access For All*

Quantum computing, with its potential to affect various sectors, also holds the promise (or peril) of reshaping our societal structures. One of the primary concerns as we transition into the quantum age is access. History provides ample evidence that groundbreaking technologies, while transformative, only sometimes distribute their benefits consistently. With the onset of quantum computing, we find ourselves at another technological crossroads.

*Digital Divide Revisited*

The introduction of the internet in the 90s brought with it hopes of democratizing information. In many ways, it succeeded. However, it also unveiled a 'digital divide', where some had access to these vast reservoirs of knowledge, and others did not. Quantum computing presents a similar scenario. Its computational capabilities can drive immense societal progress, but who gets to wield this power? And more importantly, who decides?

*Economic Implications*

The capital-intensive nature of quantum research and infrastructure means that early access may be restricted to entities with significant resources. This could result in an economic divide, where certain businesses or regions that can't afford quantum technology are left behind, leading to potential technological and economic power centralization.

*Unintended Consequences*

Like any technological revolution, the quantum leap is also riddled with unintended consequences. For instance, if quantum technology remains concentrated in the hands of a few, it might influence decision-making processes at both micro and macro levels, from local policies to international diplomatic relations. Moreover, rapid technological advancements could result in skill redundancy, challenging the current job market dynamics.

The journey into the quantum age offers many challenges and opportunities. The question isn't just about how quantum computing will reshape our world, but how we, as a global society, will ensure its benefits are reaped widely and its challenges resolved thoughtfully.

## Communication and Teaching

As the horizon of the quantum era emerges, we are presented with a compelling question: how might the interconnectedness of our world evolve? The start of the quantum internet could dissolve the very notions of time zones and geographical barriers, making one wonder if the essence of "distance" will soon be an out-of-date concept. Could we soon find ourselves in a world where global collaborations and friendships become as instantaneous as the blink of an eye?

Imagine quantum-driven virtual realities where the classroom extends far beyond four walls. A student in Chicago might walk through the bustling streets of ancient Rome, and another in Tokyo could engage with the mysteries of deep-sea ecosystems. At the same time, a curious mind in Cairo delves into the abstract wonders of quantum mechanics, all from the comfort of their homes.

Yet, while we envision these awe-inspiring prospects, we must also entertain some warning signs. As new quantum platforms reshape our social interactions, offering emotion-sensitive virtual meetings or groundbreaking social media experiences, will we unknowingly craft a divide between those immersed in this new world and those left on the fringes? Will a child who thrives in traditional learning environments feel lost in this sea of technological marvels? And as we navigate this quantum-woven world, might we risk losing the cherished nuances of face-to-face interactions?

The quantum age is not just a technical revolution; it's a profound shift in our societal fabric. As we stand on the cusp of innovation, we're challenged to ensure an ethical and vibrant future for all.

## The Challenge of Explanation

Quantum computing often feels like a riddle wrapped in a riddle. Its principles, stemming from the strange world of quantum mechanics, stand in stark contrast to our everyday experiences. How does one articulate the idea of superposition – where a quantum bit, or qubit, can exist in multiple states simultaneously – to someone accustomed to a binary world of 0s and 1s?

The challenge to simplify quantum concepts can be as difficult as describing the color blue to someone who's only ever seen in black and white. Yet, this isn't just an academic exercise or a puzzle for the curious-minded. The deeper issue lies in fostering trust and acceptance in a society already wary of technologies they barely understand. If the intricacies of today's algorithms leave many feeling in the dark, the seemingly otherworldly nature of quantum operations might seem like an impenetrable black box.

But this opacity poses a risk. When people don't understand something, they're less likely to trust it. And without trust, how can society fully embrace and integrate the potential wonders of quantum computing? For quantum tech to flourish, there's an urgency not just to advance it, but to make its complexities understandable, relatable, and ultimately, trustworthy to the masses.

## Quantum and Business

*A New Paradigm*

Bill Gates once said, "We're still in the early days of what these computers can do." Now, think of quantum computing as the next big step after our classical computers. Imagine a young entrepreneur, like today's tech-savvy teenager, starting a business with the power of quantum computers. They could do things like planning the best routes for delivery trucks in an instant or finding the perfect song for you based on your mood and the weather outside!

But it's not just the good guys who see opportunities. Where there's a chance to make money or gain power, a few people always try to cheat the system. What if scammers could use these super-fast computers to trick people out of their hard-earned cash? One known scam is AI voices that sound like loved ones and are panicked for your help. One unsuspecting grandmother sent

QUANTUM COMPUTING EXPLAINED FOR BEGINNERS

thousands of dollars to who she believed to be her granddaughter in danger, to find out later she had been scammed.

Experts like Dr. Jane Smith from QuantumTech Institute often talk about the "double-edged sword" of technology. On one side, in healthcare, we could find cures for diseases faster or predict if someone might get sick in the future. But, what if someone else could access your health data? Would you be comfortable with strangers knowing so much about you?

In the field of money and banks, these computers might help predict which stocks will go up or down. But could that same power also allow a few people to control and manipulate the market unfairly? And when we talk about robots or AIs making decisions, we have to ask: Who's in charge if they make a mistake?

So, what do you think? As we step into this new world of business powered by quantum computers, should we dive in headfirst or take a moment to think about the right and wrong ways to use this power?

Remember, as we explore these new horizons, it's always a good idea to ask questions and stay curious. After all, it's our future we're shaping!

# Thought Experiment

*Quantum-AI Optimism vs. Reality*

Let's imagine for a moment a world flooded with Quantum-AI integration. Through the lens of personal stories, let's glimpse the potential benefits and pitfalls of quantum technology.

*The Good: A Mother's Relief*

It's 2035, and Jenna rushes her six-year-old daughter, Mia, to the local health center after she falls severely ill. As the clock ticks and Jenna's anxiety mounts, the medical team employs a quantum computer to cross-reference Mia's symptoms and genetic makeup with global health databases. Within minutes, the computer identifies a rare ailment and recommends a tailored treatment plan. Mia recovers fully, and Jenna is forever grateful to the quantum age for giving her precious time with her daughter.

*Reflect:* Imagine if every child, parent, or loved one had the gift of time and health through quantum-aided diagnosis. How would that reshape our personal narratives and families?

*The Bad: The Blackout Days*

The year is 2028. A chilly evening turns sinister as major cities around the globe plunge into darkness. Quantum-empowered hackers bypass even the most advanced defenses, seizing control of power grids and nuclear facilities. Panic ensues. The world stands on the abyss, wondering if these faceless entities now possess the power to instigate global catastrophe.

*Reflect:* Picture your hometown or city in utter darkness, dependent on faceless hackers' whims. How vital is it for us to ensure our defensive technologies evolve as fast, if not faster, than our quantum capabilities?

### The Ugly: The Artist and the Quantum

In 2030, a renowned architect, Sophia, witnesses the unveiling of quantum-driven AI design software. This software can generate building designs in seconds, accounting for local climates, geographies, and cultures. While these structures are efficient, they lack the human touch—Sophia's creative flair and understanding of emotional resonance. Soon, her intricate designs are sidelined for quantum-generated blueprints. A world of artistic passion risks being overshadowed by quantum AI's sheer speed and efficiency.

*Reflect:* What if emotionless quantum algorithms suddenly outpaced the music, art, or designs you cherished? How do we balance human creativity with computational efficiency in the future?

While these scenarios may seem far-fetched, we must remember our resilience as a society. Much like the challenges posed by the invention of computers and the internet, we will learn, adapt, and harness the potential of upcoming technologies. Historically, every technological leap has not only presented challenges but also prompted innovation, creating millions of jobs and vast wealth. With their unparalleled analytical capabilities, Quantum computers may even guide us in forecasting and mitigating potential pitfalls. As with any great advancement, it's up to us to steer its potential toward the collective good.

## Embracing the Quantum Future

As we prepare to usher in a new era powered by quantum technology, the responsibility of molding this future rests not just with the experts and pioneers but with each one of us. Your curiosity, questions, and pursuit of knowledge will play a defining role in how society understands and integrates quantum advancements.

Have you considered how quantum technology could impact your daily life or profession? How might it revolutionize industries, from entertainment to finance? What precautions do we need to establish today to ensure a rewarding tomorrow?

The quantum domain is vast, intricate, and undoubtedly overwhelming at times, but the rewards of understanding even its basics can be immensely fulfilling. Start your journey now. Dive into resources like [Quantum Wonders for the Curious Mind] or attend local quantum computing workshops. Discuss with friends, join online forums, and participate in community debates.

The future is not just something that happens to us; it's something we can influence. How will you shape the quantum era? The first step is to begin exploring, questioning, and learning.

## Thoughtful Questions for Reflection

Each of these questions invites deep reflection on the role of technology in society and the moral imperatives that come with superior power. Give them some thought.

*The Privacy Paradox*

If quantum computing can decrypt most modern encryption, at what point does an individual's right to privacy become a luxury rather than a fundamental human right?

*The Quantum Divide*

As quantum advancements progress, will we unwittingly create a two-tiered society—those with quantum access and those without? Is this division morally acceptable?

*Job Ethics*

If quantum computing can render certain jobs obsolete almost overnight, is it ethical for companies to pursue such capabilities without plans for workforce retraining or support?

*The Economic Balance*

With quantum computing having the potential to reshape entire industries, do we risk placing too much power in the hands of a few corporate giants, thereby challenging the very fabric of free-market principles?

*Moral Transparency*

Given the inherent complexity of quantum mechanics, is it ethical to introduce quantum-driven solutions to the public without ensuring a basic level of understanding and informed consent?

*Corporate Quantum Responsibility*

If a corporation holds significant quantum power, does it bear a moral responsibility to use it for societal good over profit? Where is the line drawn?

*Priority Ethics*

In a world with limited quantum resources, who gets to decide which global challenges—like climate change, health crises, poverty, or hunger—are addressed first? Is it fair to prioritize one over the other?

*Safety Versus Innovation*

At what point does the pursuit of quantum breakthroughs overshadow potential safety concerns? Is pushing the boundary of knowledge worth potential societal risks?

*Eternal Memory*

With quantum-driven data storage solutions, is it morally right to have the capacity to store information indefinitely, potentially long past its relevance or even the lifespan of the individual it concerns?

*The Moral Compass of Quantum Innovation*

As we stand at the cusp of quantum advancements, do we have a moral duty to ask not just if we can, but if we should?

*The Ethical Balance of Innovation and Regulation*

In the quest for quantum advancements, is it moral to prioritize free-market innovation over potential regulatory safeguards, risking the suppression of revolutionary breakthroughs? Where does one draw the line between preserving the freedom to innovate and ensuring the collective well-being of society?

In conclusion, I recommend **three actionable steps** for you to engage with quantum computing and its ethical outcomes. First, get educated on this cutting-edge technology and its potential. By gaining a deeper understanding of quantum computing, you will contribute to informed discussions and debates surrounding its development and use.

Second, reach out to policymakers and industry leaders to advocate for responsible development and use of quantum computing. As previously discussed, numerous entities are involved in the evolution of quantum technology, and collective action is necessary to ensure that it is designed and used ethically and responsibly.

Finally, stay informed about the latest changes in quantum computing and its ethical implications by following reputable news sources and attending relevant conferences or events. By staying up-to-date on emerging trends and debates, readers can continue to engage with this groundbreaking technology and contribute to its responsible evolution and use.

# CONCLUSION

Dear Explorer,

Wow, what an adventure we've been on! From the mystical realms of quantum mechanics to the promising future of machine learning, we've traversed the thrilling landscape of tomorrow's tech. Your curiosity, perseverance, and enthusiasm have made this worth every minute.

But remember, your quantum story doesn't end here. You're now equipped with a powerful Quantum Toolkit (Chapter 6). Your new knowledge about applications, misconceptions, and algorithms can empower you to tap into the quantum world in ways you might not have imagined. I hope the insights shared in this book illuminate your path. If they did, and you found value in this book, I'd be grateful if you could leave a book review. Sharing your experiences and feedback will help guide future explorers on their quantum quest.

This is the conclusion of our book, but it's only the beginning. Keep exploring, keep questioning, and keep dreaming big.

There are infinite quantum resources available, and you picked this one. Thank you for the opportunity. To further fuel your passion and stay in the loop with the ever-evolving world of quantum developments, news, and intriguing puzzles, we warmly invite you to join our newsletter or vibrant Facebook community.

Discover more free resources at **pantheonspace.com** or engage with us at **facebook.com/pantheonspace**.

Our deepest gratitude,

The Pantheon Space Academy

# References

*06-TrainingNNsBackprop.* (n.d.).
https://srdas.github.io/DLBook2/TrainingNNsBackprop.html

10Web AI Website Builder. (2023, August 15). *Home.* 10Web. https://10web.io/

Abioye, S., Oyedele, L. O., Akanbi, L., Ajayi, A. O., Bilal, M., Akinadé, O. O., & Ahmed, A. (2021). Artificial intelligence in the construction industry: A review of present status, opportunities and future challenges. *Journal of Building Engineering, 44,* 103299. https://doi.org/10.1016/j.jobe.2021.103299

Ahmadi, H. (2012). *Quantum Algorithms For: Quantum Phase Estimation* [Pdf]. University of Central Florida. https://core.ac.uk/download/236257998.pdf

*AI for Small Business: A Beginner's Guide.* (n.d.-a). https://www.microsoft.com/en-us/microsoft-365/business-insights-ideas/resources/how-ai-help-small-business

*AI for Small Business: A Beginner's Guide.* (n.d.-b). https://www.microsoft.com/en-us/microsoft-365/business-insights-ideas/resources/how-ai-help-small-business

Aïmeur, E., Brassard, G., & Gambs, S. (2012). Quantum speed-up for unsupervised learning. *Machine Learning, 90*(2), 261–287. https://doi.org/10.1007/s10994-012-5316-5

Allison, P. R. (2023). Quantum computing: What are the data storage challenges? *ComputerWeekly.com.* https://www.computerweekly.com/feature/Quantum-computing-What-are-the-data-storage-challenges

Altman, E., Brown, K. R., Carleo, G., Carr, L. D., Demler, E., Chin, C., DeMarco, B., Economou, S. E., Eriksson, M. A., Fu, K. C., Greiner, M., Hazzard, K. R. A., Hulet, R. G., Kollár, A. J., Lev, B., Lukin, M. D., Ma, R., Mi, X., Misra, S., . . . Zwierlein, M. (2021). Quantum Simulators: architectures and opportunities. *PRX Quantum, 2*(1). https://doi.org/10.1103/prxquantum.2.017003

American Institute of Physics. (2022, April 26). *Christopher Monroe.* https://www.aip.org/history-programs/niels-bohr-library/oral-histories/46948

Amin, M. H. S., Andriyash, E., Rolfe, J. T., Kulchytskyy, B., & Melko, R. G. (2018). Quantum Boltzmann Machine. *Physical Review X, 8*(2). https://doi.org/10.1103/physrevx.8.021050

Aminpour, M., Montemagno, C., & Tuszyński, J. A. (2019). An Overview of Molecular Modeling for Drug Discovery with Specific Illustrative Examples of Applications. *Molecules, 24*(9), 1693. https://doi.org/10.3390/molecules24091693

Anderson, M. (2023). 5 Ways Artificial intelligence helps in improving website usability. *IEEE Computer Society.* https://www.computer.org/publications/tech-news/trends/5-ways-artificial-intelligence-helps-in-improving-website-usability/

*Artificial Intelligence (AI) services & Solutions.* (n.d.-a). Accenture. https://www.accenture.com/us-en/services/ai-artificial-intelligence-index

*Artificial Intelligence (AI) services & Solutions.* (n.d.-b). Accenture. https://www.accenture.com/us-en/services/ai-artificial-intelligence-index

Atske, S. (2020, July 9). *4. The internet will continue to make life better | Pew Research Center.* Pew Research Center: Internet, Science & Tech. https://www.pewresearch.org/internet/2019/10/28/4-the-internet-will-continue-to-make-life-better/

Atske, S. (2022a, September 15). *3. Improvements ahead: How humans and AI might evolve together in the next decade | Pew Research Center.* Pew Research Center: Internet, Science & Tech. https://www.pewresearch.org/internet/2018/12/10/improvements-ahead-how-humans-and-ai-might-evolve-together-in-the-next-decade/

Atske, S. (2022b, September 15). *3. Improvements ahead: How humans and AI might evolve together in the next decade | Pew Research Center.* Pew Research Center: Internet, Science & Tech. https://www.pewresearch.org/internet/2018/12/10/improvements-ahead-how-humans-and-ai-might-evolve-together-in-the-next-decade/

*Azure Quantum - Quantum Cloud Computing Service | Microsoft Azure.* (n.d.). https://azure.microsoft.com/en-us/products/quantum

Baksh, M. (2023). NIST selects 12 companies for implementing Post-Quantum cryptography. *Nextgov.com.* https://www.nextgov.com/cybersecurity/2022/07/nist-selects-12-companies-implementing-post-quantum-cryptography/374601/

Bender, A., & Cortés-Ciriano, I. (2021). Artificial intelligence in drug discovery: what is realistic, what are illusions? Part 1: Ways to make an impact, and why we are not there yet. *Drug Discovery Today, 26*(2), 511–524. https://doi.org/10.1016/j.drudis.2020.12.009

Bijaya. (2023, September 5). *Quantum computing accelerating drug discovery & development.* Experion Technologies – Software Product Engineering Services. https://experionglobal.com/quantum-computing-drug-discovery-process/

BioExcel CoE. (2022, April 6). *Application of molecular dynamics simulations in the field of drug discovery* [Video]. YouTube. https://www.youtube.com/watch?v=yNGS_mv1-94

Biswal, A. (2023). AI applications: Top 18 artificial intelligence applications in 2023. *Simplilearn.com.* https://www.simplilearn.com/tutorials/artificial-intelligence-tutorial/artificial-intelligence-applications

Brown, K. L., Munro, W. J., & Kendon, V. (2010). Using quantum computers for quantum simulation. *Entropy, 12*(11), 2268–2307. https://doi.org/10.3390/e12112268

Buchholz, S., & Ammanath, B. (2022). Quantum computing may create ethical risks for businesses. It's time to prepare. *Deloitte Insights.* https://www2.deloitte.com/uk/en/insights/topics/cyber-risk/quantum-computing-ethics-risks.html

Buntz, B. (2023). Quantum computing promises new frontier in drug discovery and bioinformatics. *Drug Discovery and Development.* https://www.drugdiscoverytrends.com/quantum-computing-drug-discovery/

Buvailo, A. (n.d.). 12 Companies Using Quantum Theory To Accelerate Drug Discovery. *www.linkedin.com.* https://www.linkedin.com/pulse/13-companies-using-quantum-theory-accelerate-drug-andrii-buvailo-

Capgemini. (2022, July 22). *What if quantum could transform & shorten the drug discovery lifecycle?* [Video]. YouTube. https://www.youtube.com/watch?v=ZzGo79mjbRk

Centre for Quantum Technologies, National University of Singapore, Clarendon Laboratory, University of Oxford, Keble College, Institute for Scientific Interchange, Johnson, T., Clark, S., & Jaksch, D. (2023). *What is a quantum simulator?* [Pdf]. Johnson et al. https://www3.physics.ox.ac.uk/groups/qubit/fetch.asp?url=groupwebsite/papers/paper311.pdf

Chow, J., Greplova, E., Heijman, F., Kuchkovsky, C., O'Halloran, D., Pointing, J., Shutko, G., & Williams, C. (2022). *State of Quantum Computing: Building a Quantum Economy* [Pdf]. World Economic Forum. https://www3.weforum.org/docs/WEF_State_of_Quantum_Computing_2022.pdf

Chui, M., Roberts, R., Rodchenko, T., Singla, A., Sukharevsky, A., Yee, L., & Zurkiya, D. (2023). What every CEO should know about generative AI. *McKinsey & Company.* https://www.mckinsey.com/capabilities/mckinsey-digital/our-insights/what-every-ceo-should-know-about-generative-ai

Chúláin, A. N. (2023, April 12). What is quantum computing and how will quantum computers change the world? *Euronews.* https://www.euronews.com/next/2023/04/12/what-is-quantum-computing-and-what-does-a-quantum-computer-do

Ciliberto, C., Herbster, M., Ialongo, A. D., Pontil, M., Rocchetto, A., Severini, S., & Wossnig, L. (2018). Quantum machine learning: a classical perspective. *Proceedings of the Royal Society A: Mathematical, Physical and Engineering Sciences, 474*(2209), 20170551. https://doi.org/10.1098/rspa.2017.0551

Cocchi, M., Minuto, C., Tonello, L., Gabrielli, F., Bernroider, G., Tuszyński, J. A., Cappello, F., & Rasenick, M. M. (2017). Linoleic acid: Is this the key that unlocks the quantum brain? Insights linking broken symmetries in molecular biology, mood disorders and personalistic emergentism. *BMC Neuroscience, 18*(1). https://doi.org/10.1186/s12868-017-0356-1

Coleman, S. (2023). Who Are You? How Bank Apps Confirm Your Identity Without Meeting You In Person. *TecSmash.* https://tecsmash.com/how-bank-apps-confirm-your-identity/

Connected World. (2023). Success stories: Quantum sensors monitor brains. *Connected World - IoT and Digital Transformation.* https://connectedworld.com/success-stories-quantum-sensors-monitor-brains/

Contributor, E. (2022). Leveraging physics and quantum computing to accelerate drug discovery. *Labiotech.eu.* https://www.labiotech.eu/interview/quantum-computing-drug-discovery/

Cox, T. (2023, July 13). Researchers demonstrate the power of quantum computing in drug design. *phys.org.* https://phys.org/news/2023-07-power-quantum-drug.html

Dallaire-Demers, P., & Killoran, N. (2018). Quantum generative adversarial networks. *Physical Review.* https://doi.org/10.1103/physreva.98.012324

Dang, Y., Jiang, N., Hu, H., Ji, Z., & Zhang, W. (2018). Image classification based on quantum K-Nearest-Neighbor algorithm. *Quantum Information Processing, 17*(9). https://doi.org/10.1007/s11128-018-2004-9

Dargan, J. (2022a). 8 online Quantum computing courses to start career in 2022. *The Quantum Insider.* https://thequantuminsider.com/2020/01/07/quantum-computing-course/

Dargan, J. (2022b). 25 Quantum Cryptography & Encryption Companies [2022]. *The Quantum Insider.* https://thequantuminsider.com/2021/01/11/25-companies-building-the-quantum-cryptography-communications-markets/

Dargan, J. (2023a). Top 63 Quantum Computer Simulators For 2022. *The Quantum Insider.* https://thequantuminsider.com/2022/06/14/top-63-quantum-computer-simulators-for-2022/

Dargan, J. (2023b). 81 Quantum computing companies: An ultimate 2023 list. *The Quantum Insider.* https://thequantuminsider.com/2022/09/05/quantum-computing-companies-ultimate-list-for-2022/

Das Sarma, S., Deng, D., & Duan, L. (2019, March). *Machine learning meets quantum physics.* pubs.aip.org. https://pubs.aip.org/physicstoday/article/72/3/48/915959/Machine-learning-meets-quantum-physicsThe-marriage

*DataRobot AI Platform | Deliver Value from AI.* (2023, October 5). DataRobot AI Platform. https://www.datarobot.com/

De Wolf, R. (2023). *Quantum Computing: Lecture Notes* [Pdf]. Independent via Amsterdam U.

Deloitte. (2022, May 17). 3 ways quantum computing may create ethical risks. *WSJ.* https://deloitte.wsj.com/cio/3-ways-quantum-computing-may-create-ethical-risks-01652815643

*Diving deep into quantum computing: modern cryptography.* (n.d.). https://www.trendmicro.com/vinfo/us/security/news/security-technology/diving-deep-into-quantum-computing-modern-cryptography

Dong, D., Chen, C., Li, H., & Tarn, T. (2008). Quantum Reinforcement learning. *IEEE Transactions on Systems, Man, and Cybernetics, 38*(5), 1207–1220. https://doi.org/10.1109/tsmcb.2008.925743

Dougfinke. (2023). Public companies. *Quantum Computing Report.* https://quantumcomputingreport.com/public-companies/

DSpace@MIT. (2021). *Quantum Simulators: Architectures and Opportunities.* American Physical Society. https://dspace.mit.edu/bitstream/handle/1721.1/142317/PRXQuantum.2.017003.pdf?sequence=2&isAllowed=y

Durrant, J. D., & McCammon, J. A. (2011). Molecular dynamics simulations and drug discovery. *BMC Biology, 9*(1). https://doi.org/10.1186/1741-7007-9-71

EastMojo, T. (2023, May 12). Quantum AI chronicles: success stories and teachable moments. *EastMojo.* https://www.eastmojo.com/science-tech/2023/05/12/quantum-ai-chronicles-success-stories-and-teachable-moments/

Editor. (n.d.). *Intel releases Quantum SDK.* https://www.i-programmer.info/news/90-tools/16134-intel-releases-quantum-sdk.html

Education. (n.d.). *Google Quantum AI.* https://quantumai.google/education

edX. (n.d.). *Delft University of Technology.* https://www.edx.org/school/delftx

Elnagar, G. N., & Kazemi, M. (1998). Pseudospectral Legendre-based optimal computation of nonlinear constrained variational problems. *Journal of Computational and Applied Mathematics, 88*(2), 363–375. https://doi.org/10.1016/s0377-0427(97)00225-2

Evans, D. (2023, June 26). 5 Websites Designed by Artificial Intelligence. *Hubspot.* https://blog.hubspot.com/website/ai-website-design-examples

Evers, M., Heid, A., & Ostojic, I. (2021). Pharma's digital Rx: Quantum computing in drug research and development. *McKinsey & Company.* https://www.mckinsey.com/industries/life-sciences/our-insights/pharmas-digital-rx-quantum-computing-in-drug-research-and-development

*First step towards Global-Scale Quantum Internet Taken.* (n.d.). A2D CONSULTING. http://www.a2d-consulting.com/digital-feed1/first-step-towards-global-scale-quantum-internet-taken

Flöther, F. F. (2023). The state of quantum computing applications in health and medicine. *arXiv (Cornell University)*. https://doi.org/10.1017/qut.2023.4

Fulton, S., III. (2020, November 10). What is quantum computing today? The how, why, and when of a paradigm shift. *ZDNET*. https://www.zdnet.com/article/what-is-quantum-computing-understanding-the-how-why-and-when-of-quantum-computers/

*Generative AI: What is it, tools, models, applications and use cases.* (n.d.). Gartner. https://www.gartner.com/en/topics/generative-ai

Gil, D., Mantas, J., Sutor, R., Townes, L., Flother, F., & Schnabel, C. (2023). Five strategies to prepare for paradigm-shifting quantum technology. *IBM.com*.

*Google Scholar.* (n.d.-a). https://scholar.google.com/scholar_lookup?title=Quantum-inspired+neural+networks&conference=Proceedings+of+the+Neural+Information+Processing+Systems+95&author=Menneer,+T.&author=Narayanan,+A.&publication_year=1995

*Google Scholar.* (n.d.-b). https://scholar.google.com/scholar_lookup?title=Algorithms+for+Quantum+Computation:+Discrete+Logarithms+and+Factoring&conference=Proceedings+of+the+35th+Annual+Symposium+on+Foundation+of+Computer+Science&author=Shor,+P.W.&publication_year=1994&pages=124%E2%80%93134

*Google Scholar.* (n.d.-c). https://scholar.google.com/scholar_lookup?title=Quantum+algorithms+for+supervised+and+unsupervised+machine+learning&author=Lloyd,+S.&author=Mohseni,+M.&author=Rebentrost,+P.&publication_year=2013&journal=arXiv

*Google Scholar.* (n.d.-d). https://scholar.google.com/scholar_lookup?title=q-means:+A+quantum+algorithm+for+unsupervised+machine+learning&author=Kerenidis,+I.&author=Landman,+J.&author=Luongo,+A.&author=Prakash,+A.&publication_year=2018&journal=arXiv

*Google Scholar.* (n.d.-e). https://scholar.google.com/scholar_lookup?title=Quantum+algorithms+for+solving+dynamic+programming+problems&author=Ronagh,+P.&publication_year=2019&journal=arXiv

*Google Scholar.* (n.d.-f). https://scholar.google.com/scholar_lookup?title=Automated+quantum+programming+via+

reinforcement+learning+for+combinatorial+optimization&author=McKiernan,+K.A.&aut
hor=Davis,+E.&author=Alam,+M.S.&author=Rigetti,+C.&publication_year=2019&journ
al=arXiv

*Google Scholar*. (n.d.-g).
https://scholar.google.com/scholar_lookup?title=Quantum+Wasserstein+generative+advers
arial+networks&author=Chakrabarti,+S.&author=Yiming,+H.&author=Li,+T.&author=F
eizi,+S.&author=Wu,+X.&publication_year=2019&journal=arXiv

GreyB, T. (2022). Top 10 companies researching quantum computing technology. *GreyB*.
https://www.greyb.com/blog/quantum-computing-companies/

Grover, L. K. (1997). Quantum mechanics helps in searching for a needle in a haystack.
*Physical Review Letters, 79*(2), 325–328. https://doi.org/10.1103/physrevlett.79.325

Gupta, S., Modgil, S., Bhatt, P. C., Jabbour, C. J. C., & Kamble, S. S. (2023). Quantum
computing led innovation for achieving a more sustainable Covid-19 healthcare industry.
*Technovation, 120*, 102544. https://doi.org/10.1016/j.technovation.2022.102544

Haney, B. (2021). *Quantum Machine Learning: A Patent Review* (Vol. 12) [Pdf]. Journal of
Law, Technology & The Internet.
https://scholarlycommons.law.case.edu/cgi/viewcontent.cgi?article=1131&context=jolti

Harrow, A. W., Hassidim, A., & Lloyd, S. (2009). Quantum Algorithm for linear systems
of equations. *Physical Review Letters, 103*(15).
https://doi.org/10.1103/physrevlett.103.150502

Henderson, M., Shakya, S., Pradhan, S., & Cook, T. (2020). Quanvolutional neural
networks: powering image recognition with quantum circuits. *Quantum Machine
Intelligence, 2*(1). https://doi.org/10.1007/s42484-020-00012-y

*Home*. (n.d.). https://www.oecd-ilibrary.org/sites/bb167041-
en/1/3/11/index.html?itemId=/content/publication/bb167041-
en&_csp_=509e10cb8ea8559b6f9cc53015e8814d&itemIGO=oecd&itemContentType=b
ook

*How artificial intelligence is transforming the world | Brookings*. (2023, June 27). Brookings.
https://www.brookings.edu/articles/how-artificial-intelligence-is-transforming-the-world/

Huang, H., Du, Y., Gong, M., Zhao, Y., Wu, Y., Wang, C., Li, S., Liang, F., Lin, J., Xu, Y., Yang, R., Liu, T., Hsieh, M., Deng, H., Rong, H., Peng, C., Lu, C., Chen, Y., Tao, D., . . . Pan, J. (2021). Experimental quantum generative adversarial networks for image Generation. *Physical Review Applied, 16*(2). https://doi.org/10.1103/physrevapplied.16.024051

Ibm. (n.d.). *The quest to understand what sews the universe together | IBM.* IBM. https://www.ibm.com/case-studies/cern/

*IBM Quantum Computing.* (n.d.). https://www.ibm.com/quantum

Johnson, T. H., Clark, S. R. L., & Jaksch, D. (2014). What is a quantum simulator? *EPJ Quantum Technology, 1*(1). https://doi.org/10.1140/epjqt10

Kavanagh, C. (2019). New tech, new threats, and new governance challenges: an opportunity to craft smarter responses? *Carnegie Endowment for International Peace.* https://carnegieendowment.org/2019/08/28/new-tech-new-threats-and-new-governance-challenges-opportunity-to-craft-smarter-responses-pub-79736

Kieferová, M., & Wiebe, N. (2017). Tomography and generative training with quantum Boltzmann machines. *Physical Review, 96*(6). https://doi.org/10.1103/physreva.96.062327

Ksupasate. (2023, March 12). Unleashing the Power of Quantum Computing for Machine Learning: How Quantum Machine Learning is Solving Problems Faster and Better Than Ever Before. *Medium.* https://ksupasate.medium.com/unleashing-the-power-of-quantum-computing-for-machine-learning-how-quantum-machine-learning-is-5bea3922133b?source=post_internal_links---------2----------------------------

*Learn Quantum Computing on Brilliant.* (n.d.). https://brilliant.org/courses/quantum-computing/

Lewis, J. A., & Wood, G. (2023). *Quantum Technology: applications and implications.* https://www.csis.org/analysis/quantum-technology-applications-and-implications

Lloyd, S. (1982). Least squares quantization in PCM. *IEEE Transactions on Information Theory, 28*(2), 129–137. https://doi.org/10.1109/tit.1982.1056489

Lloyd, S., Mohseni, M., & Rebentrost, P. (2014). Quantum principal component analysis. *Nature Physics, 10*(9), 631–633. https://doi.org/10.1038/nphys3029

Lloyd, S., & Weedbrook, C. (2018). Quantum Generative Adversarial Learning. *Physical Review Letters, 121*(4). https://doi.org/10.1103/physrevlett.121.040502

Lu, S., & Braunstein, S. L. (2013). Quantum decision tree classifier. *Quantum Information Processing, 13*(3), 757–770. https://doi.org/10.1007/s11128-013-0687-5

McKinsey & Company. (2021). *Quantum Computing: An Emerging Ecosystem and Industry Use Cases* [Pdf]. https://www.mckinsey.com/~/media/mckinsey/business%20functions/mckinsey%20digital/our%20insights/quantum%20computing%20use%20cases%20are%20getting%20real%20what%20you%20need%20to%20know/quantum-computing-an-emerging-ecosystem.pdf

McLean, D. (2023a). 7 Best AI SEO tools in 2023 (Reviewed & compared). *Elegant Themes Blog.* https://www.elegantthemes.com/blog/business/best-ai-seo-tools

McLean, D. (2023b). 7 Best AI SEO tools in 2023 (Reviewed & compared). *Elegant Themes Blog.* https://www.elegantthemes.com/blog/business/best-ai-seo-tools

*Michigan State University Artificial Intelligence Boot Camp - Michigan State University boot camps.* (2023, August 1). Michigan State University Boot Camps. https://bootcamp.msu.edu/artificial-intelligence/

Musti, A. (2022). Quantum Machine Learning Is The Next Big Thing. *The Quantum Insider.* https://thequantuminsider.com/2020/05/28/quantum-machine-learning-is-the-next-big-thing/

National Academies of Sciences, Engineering, and Medicine. (2019). *Quantum Computing: Progress and Prospects* [Pdf]. The National Academy of Sciences. https://doi.org/10.17226/25196

Obata, A. (2023, February 1). 10 Online Courses You Can Take To Help You Understand Quantum Computing — Quantum Zeitgeist. *Quantum Zeitgeist.* https://quantumzeitgeist.com/10-online-courses-you-can-take-to-help-you-understand-quantum-computing/

O'Connell, B., & McVearry, R. (2023, September 19). 8 Best Quantum Computing Stocks to buy in 2023. *US News & World Report.* https://money.usnews.com/investing/stock-market-news/articles/best-quantum-computing-stocks-to-buy

Parker, E., Gonzales, D., Kochhar, A., Litterer, S., O'Connor, K., Schmid, J., Scholl, K., Silberglitt, R., Chang, J., Eusebi, C., & Harold, S. (2022). *An Assessment of the U.S. and Chinese Industrial Bases in Quantum Technology* [Pdf]. RAND Corporation. https://www.rand.org/content/dam/rand/pubs/research_reports/RRA800/RRA869-1/RAND_RRA869-1.pdf

Pijselman, M. (2022). Why innovation leaders must consider quantum ethics. *www.ey.com*. https://www.ey.com/en_uk/emerging-technologies/why-innovation-leaders-must-consider-quantum-ethics

Possati, L. M. (2023). Ethics of Quantum Computing: an Outline. *Philosophy & Technology*, *36*(3). https://doi.org/10.1007/s13347-023-00651-6

Qiskit. (2022a, January 6). How Do You Explain Quantum Computing To Your Dog (And Other Important People in Your Life)? *Medium*. https://medium.com/qiskit/how-do-you-explain-quantum-computing-to-your-dog-and-other-important-people-in-your-life-22f5fdacaf11

Qiskit. (2022b, January 7). Building a quantum variational classifier using Real World data. *Medium*. https://medium.com/qiskit/building-a-quantum-variational-classifier-using-real-world-data-809c59eb17c2

*Quantum Computers: Opportunities, risks, and challenges for policymakers.* (2021, November 16). American University. https://www.american.edu/sis/centers/security-technology/quantum-computers.cfm

*Quantum computing.* (n.d.). BCG Global. https://www.bcg.com/capabilities/digital-technology-data/emerging-technologies/quantum-computing

Quantum computing use cases are getting real—what you need to know. (2021). In *McKinsey & Company*. https://www.mckinsey.com/capabilities/mckinsey-digital/our-insights/quantum-computing-use-cases-are-getting-real-what-you-need-to-know

*Quantum Information Science and Engineering Research at NSF | NSF - National Science Foundation.* (n.d.). https://www.nsf.gov/mps/quantum/quantum_research_at_nsf.jsp

*Quantum Learning Machine - ATOS.* (2023, July 26). Atos. https://atos.net/en/solutions/quantum-learning-machine

*Quantum Science, networking, and Communications.* (2023, October 5). University of Chicago Professional Education. https://professional.uchicago.edu/find-your-fit/courses/quantum-science-networking-and-communications

*Real World Drug Discovery: A Chemist's Guide to Biotech and Pharmaceutical research: Rydzewski, Robert M.: 9780080466170: Amazon.com: Books.* (n.d.). https://www.amazon.com/Real-World-Drug-Discovery-Pharmaceutical/dp/0080466176

Rebentrost, P., Mohseni, M., & Lloyd, S. (2014). Quantum Support vector machine for big data classification. *Physical Review Letters, 113*(13). https://doi.org/10.1103/physrevlett.113.130503

*Researchers take a step toward novel quantum simulators | SLAC National Accelerator Laboratory.* (2023, January 30). SLAC National Accelerator Laboratory. https://www6.slac.stanford.edu/news/2023-01-30-researchers-take-step-toward-novel-quantum-simulators

Roundy, J. (2023). 10 companies building quantum computers. *Data Center.* https://www.techtarget.com/searchdatacenter/feature/Companies-building-quantum-computers

Ruane, J. (2021, December 14). *Quantum computing for business leaders.* Harvard Business Review. https://hbr.org/2022/01/quantum-computing-for-business-leaders

Salo-Ahen, O. M. H., Alanko, I., Bhadane, R., Bonvin, A. M. J. J., Honorato, R. V., Hossain, S., Juffer, A. H., Kabedev, A., Lahtela-Kakkonen, M., Larsen, A. S., Lescrinier, E., Marimuthu, P., Mirza, M. U., Mustafa, G., Nunes-Alves, A., Pantsar, T., Saadabadi, A., Singaravelu, K., & Vanmeert, M. (2020). Molecular dynamics simulations in drug discovery and pharmaceutical development. *Processes, 9*(1), 71. https://doi.org/10.3390/pr9010071

Schuld, M., Sinayskiy, I., & Petruccione, F. (2016). Prediction by linear regression on a quantum computer. *Physical Review, 94*(2). https://doi.org/10.1103/physreva.94.022342

Simons Institute. (2018, June 12). *Quantum simulators: Where do we stand?* [Video]. YouTube. https://www.youtube.com/watch?v=3EvW4_bAQDo

Situ, H., He, Z., Wang, Y., Li, L., & Zheng, S. (2020). Quantum generative adversarial network for generating discrete distribution. *Information Sciences, 538*, 193–208. https://doi.org/10.1016/j.ins.2020.05.127

Socialty Pro. (2022, September 17). *10 INSANE AI Websites that will Change the way we do Business. . .FOREVER* [Video]. YouTube. https://www.youtube.com/watch?v=iM8Fjh3pE5w

SoniaLopezBravo. (2023, June 21). *Understanding quantum computing - Azure Quantum.* Microsoft Learn. https://learn.microsoft.com/en-us/azure/quantum/overview-understanding-quantum-computing

Steer-Stephenson, C. (2022). Healthcare, finance and the impact of quantum computing tech. *Technology Magazine.* https://technologymagazine.com/enterprise-it/healthcare-finance-and-the-impact-of-quantum-computing-tech

Swayne, M. (2021). TQD Exclusive: John Martinis on quantum computing ethics and how they may offer Real-World solutions to world's biggest challenges. *The Quantum Insider.* https://thequantuminsider.com/2021/04/26/tqd-exclusive-john-martinis-on-quantum-computing-ethics-and-how-they-may-offer-real-world-solutions-to-worlds-biggest-challenges/

Swayne, M. (2023a). What Are The Remaining Challenges of Quantum Computing? *The Quantum Insider.* https://thequantuminsider.com/2023/03/24/quantum-computing-challenges/

Swayne, M. (2023b). BTQ patents innovative method and system for generating private cryptographic keys. *The Quantum Insider.* https://thequantuminsider.com/2023/06/27/btq-patents-innovative-method-and-system-for-generating-private-cryptographic-keys/

*The rise of quantum computing.* (2023, May 19). McKinsey & Company. https://www.mckinsey.com/featured-insights/the-rise-of-quantum-computing

Vakoch, D. (2012). *Archaeology, Anthropology, and Interstellar Communication* [Pdf]. National Aeronautics and Space Administration. https://www.nasa.gov/sites/default/files/files/Archaeology_Anthropology_and_Interstellar_Communication_TAGGED.pdf

Vasques, X., Paik, H., & Cif, L. (2023). Application of quantum machine learning using quantum kernel algorithms on multiclass neuron M-type classification. *Scientific Reports, 13*(1). https://doi.org/10.1038/s41598-023-38558-z

Walsh, B. (2021). Charting an ethical path for quantum computing. *Axios.*
https://www.axios.com/2021/12/11/quantum-computing-ethical-questions

*What Are The Most Promising Real-World Applications For Quantum Machine Learning.*
(n.d.). Quantum Computing Stack Exchange.
https://quantumcomputing.stackexchange.com/questions/11530/what-are-the-most-
promising-real-world-applications-for-quantum-machine-learning

*What is Quantum Computing?* | *IBM.* (n.d.). https://www.ibm.com/topics/quantum-
computing

*What is Quantum Computing? - Quantum Computing Explained - AWS.* (n.d.). Amazon
Web Services, Inc. https://aws.amazon.com/what-is/quantum-computing/

*What Makes Quantum Computing So Hard to Explain?* (2021, November 30). Quanta
Magazine. https://www.quantamagazine.org/why-is-quantum-computing-so-hard-to-
explain-20210608/

Wiebe, N., Kapoor, A., & Svore, K. M. (2015). Quantum algorithms for nearest-neighbor
methods for supervised and unsupervised learning. *Quantum Information & Computation,*
*15*(3 & 4), 316–356. https://doi.org/10.26421/qic15.3-4-7

Wikipedia contributors. (2023a). Quantum simulator. *Wikipedia.*
https://en.wikipedia.org/wiki/Quantum_simulator

Wikipedia contributors. (2023b). Quantum simulator. *Wikipedia.*
https://en.wikipedia.org/wiki/Quantum_simulator

Wikipedia contributors. (2023c). List of companies involved in quantum computing or
communication. *Wikipedia.*
https://en.wikipedia.org/wiki/List_of_companies_involved_in_quantum_computing_or_c
ommunication

WIRED. (2018, June 25). *Quantum computing expert explains one concept in 5 levels of*
*difficulty* | *WIRED* [Video]. YouTube.
https://www.youtube.com/watch?v=OWJCfOvochA

Wong, T. (2022). *Introduction to Classical Computing.* Rooted Grove.
https://www.thomaswong.net/introduction-to-classical-and-quantum-computing-1e3p.pdf

Zapata Computing. (2022, December 7). *Zapata Computing earns two new patents for quantum Cybersecurity Threat Intelligence - Zapata AI*. Zapata AI. https://zapata.ai/news/zapata-computing-earns-two-new-patents-for-quantum-cybersecurity-threat-intelligence/

Zeguendry, A., Jarir, Z., & Quafafou, M. (2023). Quantum Machine Learning: a review and case studies. *Entropy, 25*(2), 287. https://doi.org/10.3390/e25020287

Printed in Great Britain
by Amazon

39507957R00192